MW00603808

First Cry in the Night

My Experiences as an Obstetrician and Gynecologist

Navid Darius Yazdi, MD

FIRST CRY IN THE NIGHT

For information contact:

CIANDY Associates, LLC
POB 5097
Aloha, Oregon 97006

Book and cover design by CIANDY Associates, LLC
Printed in the United States

ISBN: 978-1-7348034-0-2

First Edition: November 2021

10 9 8 7 6 5 4 3 2 1

Looking back, I am surprised at some of the fascinating and unique cases that I came across during my practice, especially when one considers that the majority of my experience revolved around a private practice in a small midwestern community. I've written down what I consider to be interesting cases and circumstances, with an intertwined mixture of medical information on female reproduction and development. I've always been surprised at how little some woman, especially young women, know about their bodies and how things function. The medical information is accurate and up to date to the best of my knowledge, at the time of this writing.

* * *

While writing this book I've tried really hard to avoid statistics, for a couple of reasons. First and foremost is the fact that for people outside of medicine, rummaging thru relevant statistics is guaranteed to induce glassy-eyed stupor. Second is the fact that in any published text, quoting statistics is a sure way to look misinformed, since the necessary lag period from writing to editing to publication runs the risk of any valid statistic becoming invalid with the passage of time. However, I have included a small collection of relevant statistics which I felt would be stable in the short term, and possibly of interest to the reader. They will be found in the last chapter, out of sight.

* * *

The memories revealed in this book are all personal experiences of an active Obstetrician and Gynecologist, during training and subsequent decades of private practice. The names and identifying features have been altered to protect the privacy of the patients, and I have taken the liberty of occasionally combining one or two separate events into one. But I assure the reader that all of the experiences are true – there are no liberties taken with the facts, and no embellishments here whatsoever. If some of the stories sound unbelievable or preposterous, such is life.

"Wherever the art of Medicine is loved,

there is also a love of Humanity"

Hippocrates

Preface

How did I get here, and what exactly am I expected to do?

It was a late afternoon in the middle of the week, in my fourth year of Medical School. I was at the hospital dropping off some lab results on the Obstetrical floor where I had previously, in casual conversation to the floor nurses, expressed an interest in Obstetrics and Gynecology. Apparently, this information had been passed on to a local practicing physician. He was at that moment gowned and ready in a private room in anticipation of an imminent delivery, and finding out that I was at the nurses' station and knowing my previously expressed interest, had requested my attendance. Great. I would love to watch a vaginal delivery from the physician's point of view[1].

But what is this?

Upon entering the room, I was told to quickly wash my hands and put on a sterile gown, gloves, and mask. It would appear that he wants me to be more involved in the delivery. Great. I get to watch from up close, maybe even assist a bit.

But what is this?

After my third attempt at properly scrubbing and covering myself with gown and gloves without cross contamination, and noting the smirks of the nurses in attendance, the physician stands up and directs me to sit on the stool directly facing the patient, whose legs are up in stirrups, her

---

[1] At this point in my life, I was the father of two boys. I attended the first delivery, missed the second, but I only observed what was going on by standing next to my wife at the head of the bed, and my point of view was similar to hers.

bottom cleansed and shaved and hanging over the edge of the bed, and a dark, completely foreign object beginning to protrude from her spreading labia. The slow, intermittent progression of this object was accompanied by loud grunts, groans, screams and other sounds of pain and displeasure from her. The Attending Physician, whom I had briefly met in the past, was of Italian descent, with a thick accent reminiscent of exaggerated amateurish acting in a low budget Mafia movie.

Surely he doesn't expect me to do the delivery – something I had remotely read about, but never studied in any detail.

But it is becoming clear that is precisely his plan for the evening. Either he intends to fan the flames of my interest in the field, or alternatively, and more likely, to make me go away somewhere else. No time to figure out his true motives, for the patient's noises are getting louder, her squeals and screams more persistent, and the bulge from her genital opening is continuing to grow in diameter while I watch with utter fascination.

Is this even possible?

Does any part of the human body stretch this much without tears and rupture? I had a pet snake once, and was amazed at the extent to which its jaws would stretch while swallowing an oversized meal. This is reminiscent, but in reverse, as if the snake were regurgitating a massive meal that it had found indigestible. But surely no snake ever swallowed or upchucked anything this much out of proportion to its size. And yet the opening of the vagina continues to gape further, and the dark object, now recognizable as a head of fine, dense black hair, continues to protrude. And distinguishable amongst the patient's crescendo screams (can anyone blame her?) the nurse's encouragements to continue pushing harder (Harder? Surely something is going to burst at the seams any second!) and the electronic sounds of the surrounding machines,

I can now distinguish the quiet and steady directions of the Attending Physician in my ear, directing me to hold a towel over my hand and maintain contact with the patient thus, and place my other hand thus, as the baby continues to crown. And my feet are beginning to uncontrollably tap, driven by pleasure and excitement.

But mostly fear.

Fear of doing something to embarrass myself and reveal my total ignorance to the world, for whatever happens here will be told, embellished and retold far and wide withing the walls of the institution in which I have another six months of education to complete; fear of doing something stupid and causing needless pain and suffering to a complete stranger; fear of getting hit in the chest by the object now beginning to protrude even further from the patient's body, driven by some incredible expulsive force; but most of all, fear of mishandling something alive and fragile and incredibly precious. And none of this is helped by the Attending Physician whose voice is now a repetitive series of instructions that are impossible to follow, given the cacophonous excitement of the moment.

And here it comes!

Finally, the head is completely out, and a suction bulb is hurriedly pressed into my hand. I know I'm supposed to suction the fluids out of the baby's mouth and nose, but how? Do I limit myself to the area around the lips and nostrils (difficult to see, since the baby at this moment is looking down at the floor), or do I push the tip into the mouth, or all the way into the back of the throat? And in my excitement and confusion at the expectant moment, I manage to use the device in reverse, putting the tip into the baby's mouth first and then squeezing the bulb, essentially pushing the secretions further back into the baby's throat. More admonishments from the Attending Physician, and undoubtedly more gossip fodder and comic relief for the brutally heartless and merciless attending nurses[1].

And now the shoulders are delivering, followed rapidly by the remainder of the baby, closely followed by a voluminous gush of fluid of mixed consistency and varied color, from the thick near blackness of meconium, to an impressive amount of bright red blood, to a Niagara of clear, warm fluid that runs down the drapes and finds its way into my shoes.

No matter, for now the baby is in my lap, facing up, which makes it possible to properly suction its mouth. It is squinting at the bright light, squirming, moving its arms, legs and head in random directions, and crying the shrill cry of the newborn, which is apparently music to the ears of the new mother, who is attempting to sit up, while her legs are still in the stirrups and her bottom hanging over the edge, and more closely examine her creation. The baby is the center of her universe, and she is ignorant of the possibility that at any moment she may slip off the end of the delivery bed, and end up in the drape pouch containing the gallons of warm, bloody fluid that moments before were gushing out of her.

---

[1] Throughout this book the reader may notice that during my training phase I refer to Nurses in what appears superficially to be less than complimentary terms. It's important that this is taken in context, for the reason has to do with the hierarchy in teaching hospitals. Doctors in training – interns and residents – are at the absolute bottom of the totem pole, and the nursing staff is generally impatient with the interference in their work and intolerant of their mistakes. In turn the student physicians stand in awe and cower in fear of the nursing staff. However, make no mistake: By and far, nurses are competent, compassionate, incredibly skilled, and knowledgeable out of proportion to their recognition or compensation. On more occasions than I can ever count or recall, I was saved from grief by an observant and assertive nurse.

The Attending Physician clamps and cuts the cord, thereby officially crowning the newborn as an independent living being. At this point I know I'm to arise and carry the baby to the warmer and the care of the skilled and impatient nursery staff, but the blotchy, bloody, bellowing creature in my lap holds such fascination that I impulsively want to delay the transfer and hold the moment for as long as possible. But the moment has passed, and I need to ensure the baby's continuing care.

And now my ears detect a new repetitive admonishment, in that thick Italian accent, from the Attending Physician standing behind me:

"Yazdi, don't drop the baby!";

"Yazdi, you drop the baby and I will kill you!";

"Don't drop the baby!"

Drop the baby?

I would protect this squealing, squirming, slippery, and utterly helpless creature unhesitatingly with my life!

I cradle it in my arms, carry it over the warmer, ever so gently set it down, gaze upon it for a moment longer than necessary, and return to the position facing the patient's bottom, now a mass of oozing blood and torn tissues. The remainder of that day is long forgotten, but the excitement of that moment never faded over the next three decades. For in that moment, I unwaveringly decided this is what I want to wake up knowing I will be doing every day.

Contents

First Cry in the Night

The Profession

The practice of medicine has traditionally held a position of high regard in society. In surveys going back decades, physicians have always been held in positions of high trust, just behind family, and alongside nurses, clergy, and firemen[1]. In turn physicians have had a special relationship with their patients, with an ingrained sense of duty. There were always some bad apples, and the profession had its share of predators, cheats, crooks and other miscreants, but in significantly less numbers than would be expected. One of the contributing factors must have been the long struggle to gain the title. A predator, cheat or crook will not spend a decade getting a medical degree, for there are far easier ways to make a living, legal or otherwise.

* * *

My parents were both physicians, establishing themselves in the early 1970's. My father was a surgeon, a specialist. As such, he did not have a long-term relationship with his patients, the majority of whom were referred to his care by other physicians. His success therefore depended not only on his skills, which were unfortunately unremarkable, but on his interpersonal relationship with his peers, which was never adequately developed. As a result, he struggled throughout his short career.

My mother on the other hand was a pediatrician, a primary care provider. The primary care physician establishes a long-term relationship with their patients, not only taking care of them during times of illness, but often serving as a support person during times of hardship and stress. In the 1970's, a physician could allow a personal relationship to develop alongside the professional one. This often resulted in a strong sense of

---

[1] The rankings have significantly changed since the new millennium, undoubtedly from the widespread publicity of bad behavior on the part of a few members, and feigned ignorance on the part of many.

duty and responsibility toward the patients' health, both physical and mental. In turn, it would elevate the physician into a position of incredible power over the patient, a position that inevitably would lead to abuse in some instances. When these abuses came to light, even in egregious cases, they would often be ignored, minimized or denied by colleagues and oversight boards, in a misguided attempt to maintain the sheen of the profession. The same logic led to incompetent physicians being able to continue to practice by moving to another community, or in cases of gross incompetence, to another state[1].

However, it wasn't always done to protect the profession. I am personally guilty of allowing incompetent behavior to go unreported, while struggling to balance my sense of duty to someone who wasn't my patient with the need to continue to work with the individual physician, in our small community.

The worst case that comes to mind involved a pediatrician who performed a circumcision on the wrong newborn, one whose parents, for social and religious reasons, did not believe in the procedure. When he realized his error, he proceeded to convince the parents to sign a consent after the fact by spouting false data and convincing arguments about the benefits and necessity of the procedure. The parents, unsophisticated agricultural workers, overwhelmed by arguments of the highly educated and trained professional, eventually relented. I also saw errors during surgical procedures that resulted in complications, and observed the offending physicians cover up during their dictation of the operative

---

[1] Similar to the mechanism that protected predatory priests for decades, another profession that was held in a comparable position of high regard and trust in the community.

report. The patients all eventually recovered, and my internal struggle resolved itself.

Another case that weighed heavily on me (even though I was not directly involved in the patient's care) involved the infertility patient of a colleague. Apparently after an extensive workup that did not reveal any basis for the problem, the patient was scheduled for a diagnostic laparoscopy. This is an outpatient procedure during which a small camera and one or more small manipulators are inserted into the patient's abdomen in order to examine the reproductive organ and try and identify a cause for the infertility. Since the uterus needs to be moved about, the cervix is dilated and a manipulator is inserted into the cavity of the uterus. Also, as part of the procedure, a dye is injected therein and pushed into the uterus and thru the Fallopian tubes to confirm that they are open throughout. As with any surgical procedure on a reproductive age woman, even one with an infertility diagnosis, a pregnancy test is always performed, usually within a 24-hour window prior to surgery. In this case the test was done in the office the day before. The surgery was completed without complication, but afterwards it was noted that the office pregnancy test was positive. Why it wasn't checked prior to surgery was never explained, but apparently the patient was carrying a very early pregnancy while her uterus was invaded with the manipulator and dye forced thru, during an examination designed to identify a cause for infertility. The irony was not lost on those in the know, although the patient was never told of the lab results. She only became aware during a second pregnancy test at her follow-up visit a week later, and of course she was elated, and no doubt gave undeserved credit to her physician.

As for the outcome, she miscarried a couple of weeks later. Early pregnancy losses are very common, and even more so in infertility patients, and this was my rationalization for not standing up as the patient's advocate.

My own guilty example was a repeat cesarean that I performed on an immigrant mother pregnant with her second child. She and her husband had a very limited command of English, having recently immigrated from Eastern Europe, and it somehow came across that her first delivery was by Cesarean[1]. She had a crease on her lower abdomen that resembled a well healed scar, and so the die was cast. At her delivery, I was surprised at her perfect internal anatomy, free of the scars or adhesions that would be expected from a previous surgery, and my physician assistant also questioned the history of previous Cesarean[2]. My suspicions were finally confirmed during her uncomplicated recovery when the new parents, struggling to overcome the language barrier, made it clear that they were surprised how painful this delivery was and how long the recovery took compared to the first time. Knowing I was guilty of performing a procedure without proper consent (legally guilty of assault, as it were), and having condemned the mother to future cesarean deliveries, I struggled with what to do and how to go about righting the terrible wrong. I finally contacted the risk assessment supervisor at the hospital (the other guilty party, their employees having obtained the surgical consent without properly overcoming the language barrier and ensuring that the patient clearly and completely understood the proposed procedure) and confessed with the details. She called back a day later, after

---

[1] This was during a time when a trial of labor after Cesarean was considered unacceptable.
[2] And of course, being a good colleague, he made his comments to me in private and didn't follow up on anything.

having reviewed the case with the appropriate committee (and undoubtedly an attorney or two) and recommended not saying anything further since there were no complications. I jumped at the opportunity to avoid adverse publicity and a blight on my record. The patient soon moved and I did not see them again after their follow-up visit (they were still expressing gratitude for the care received, which only served to make things worse). The guilt however will not go away, and 30 years later if I could find that lovely lady and her devoted husband, I would offer my deepest, sincerest apology and beg forgiveness for violating their trust, cowardly taking the easy road, and putting them thru the unnecessary expense and pain and suffering during that and subsequent deliveries.

* * *

My medical career spanned 25 years, and sat at the cusp of a tsunamic change in the practice of medicine. Now, looking back, it's easy to see that the change was gradual enough not to draw undue attention. The older physicians that didn't like the changes retired, the younger ones did not know any different, and the large middle group accepted the changes as they came on in small steps. Many of the changes were for the better, many were necessary to allow the supervisory boards to do their jobs, and many were mandated to reign in the ever-increasing costs of medical care. Combined with the increasing need to balance the lifestyle of the physicians[1], and the shift to a business model with increasing emphasis on

---

[1] The ultimate form is the hospitalist, or on the Obstetrical unit, Laborists. These are physicians hired by hospitals to take care of patients upon admission. The primary physicians thus only work a typical day during the week without call duties, and sleep soundly at night, knowing that any patients in labor will be in the care of the Laborist, who will admit, deliver, and discharge the patient. This was inconceivable in my era, and my patients would have rioted at the suggestion.

the bottom line, the change in the physician-patient relationship became palpable and inevitable, and not necessarily positive.

The chasm between the physician and patients continues to grow, and is accelerated by the increasing volume of information – accurate or false – available on the internet. Suddenly, the physicians, who for centuries were respected for their experience and depth of knowledge, knew less about a specific subject that the prepared patient. And so, the social stature of the physician continues to diminish.

* * *

The federal government, in order to form a correlation between quality of care and reimbursement, came up with extensive lists of parameters that needed to be complied with in order to justify the documented level of care and subsequent billing level and reimbursement. Suddenly physicians, most of whom by their nature enjoy patient interactions, found themselves spending as much time on electronic records as they did in face-to-face time spent with their patients. By one measure, primary care physicians spend 45 minutes or longer doing the necessary paperwork for every 60 minutes of patient interaction time. The productivity pressures thus created lead to diminished social time with the patients, which makes the patients in turn feel rushed and their concerns irrelevant. The net result is that the physicians feel more like a businessman, and the patients feel neglected and are quicker to seek redress in real or perceived cases of mistakes. Once upon a time, if the physician made a minor mistake or was guilty of an oversight, they confessed and apologized, and the patient, more likely than not, accepted the apology and moved on. But now that it's a business, the physicians are quick to draw up the defensive drawbridges, and the relationship with the patients rapidly becomes adversarial. The subsequent settlement awards inevitably raise the malpractice premiums – for many specialists the single largest overhead – and thus the cycle continues.

* * *

One situation that I found bizarre involved a quirk in billing and reimbursement for office visits and medical procedures.

As a solo practitioner, I worked under three general reimbursement categories[1]. These were government managed plans, private insurance plans, and self-pay individuals.

First, there were Federal and State payment plans, Medicare and Medicaid, respectively. The Federal level of reimbursement was inadequate to pay the overhead[2], and Medicare patients were scheduled as a service to the community[3]. A solo practitioner limited to only Medicare patients, and continuing to operate in the traditional manner, will soon find themselves in debt. Traditional in this case means taking the time to listen to and address any concerns, dealing with a multitude of complaints at one visit, and willingness to take the time to socialize and get to know the patient beyond just a medical case. Today, the only way to make the Federal payment system work is by scheduling routine patient visits in fifteen minute slots, limiting visits to one problem, and if any other problems or issues are brought up, to reschedule for another visit. Current medical practices with large Medicaid populations typically operate as an

---

[1] This is true of most medical offices and practitioners.
[2] Overhead in my solo Obstetrics & Gynecology practice ran about 80%, and I was told this was typical. It comes down markedly with more practitioners, and is zero in managed offices under contract to a health care providing entity.
[3] This is the reason many private practitioners limit the number of Medicare patients, and some will not schedule them at all.

assembly line, and shift much of the care of the patient to assistants, such as aides, Med-Techs, or Nurse Practitioners.

State reimbursements were somewhat better, but still meager. The best reimbursements were via private insurance. During my era of practice, it was not unusual to find private insurance paying whatever was billed to the patient for a given service, without question or negotiation. The result was that the base charge for any procedure (office or surgical), was maximized to take advantage of these reimbursement opportunities. This had no bearing on the charges to the managed care patients, as these were fixed and were billed at rates set in the contracts. The onerous burden fell upon the self-pay patients. They couldn't be billed at a reduced rate (since that would expose the physician to charges of fraud, for billing insurance at a higher rate for the same service), and they were not protected by prearranged billing contracts.

And thus, it came to pass that the people that could least afford medical care were saddled with the largest bills for any given service.

In my community today, a simple, uncomplicated delivery will cost about $18,000 total[1]. This includes the fee of the physician as well as associated hospital fees for delivery and recovery for one day. Self-pay patients will be billed for the entire amount, in contrast to the $500 to $2500 billed to those with insurance contracts and deductibles, and up to $5000 to those with minimal, catastrophic insurance coverage[2].

---

[1] The total rises rapidly with any complications, even minor ones, as hospitals scramble to take advantage of billing opportunities. Who can forget the stories about the $30 hospital charge for a Tylenol, and another $10 for its plastic dispensing cup.

[2] See page-203 for an interesting historical comparison.

The Background

To this day, I don't know how my mother did it[1]. She was born and raised in Iran, in an era when girls were viewed as a burden by their families, to be married off as soon as possible and legal, and as a baby machine, cook, and housekeeper by their spouses. And expressing a desire to pursue higher education before marriage resulted in expressions of disdain and a firm lecture from the parents, and if brought up after marriage it was met with hearty ridicule, additional household chores (for obviously she has too much free time on her hands) or in extreme cases, physical punishment.

* * *

And yet, even in her late teens, my mother was steadfast in her desire to become a physician, and did not waver even after getting married and having two boys. In Iran, in spite of the political climate and her duties as a mother and home keeper, she managed to continue her education after high school. When the family immigrated to the United States in the mid-1960's, she managed to get accepted to Medical School in New Jersey, followed by a Residency in Pediatrics.

My father led her in his medical education while pursuing a career as a surgeon, but my mother was undoubtedly the driving force in the family. My father was an average surgeon, failing his board certification test multiple times and, as a result, being forced to practice in a small town in Wyoming while the rest of the family continued to live in New Jersey.

My mother on the other hand, came to excel as a Board-Certified Pediatrician. After her Residency training was completed, she went into private practice, and rapidly achieved a rare level of success – not in a

---

[1] Monireh Mahboubi, MD. A storied Middle Eastern name.

monetary sense, but by the unwavering adoration of her patients[1], gaining the respect of her colleagues (at a time when female physicians were still a rarity, even in the United States), and the admiration of the hospital staff. During the Christmas holidays, our house was filled with tokens of appreciation from her grateful patients, and for good reason. She viewed the children never as a burden, but as members of the family[2]. As a result, she was willing to care for them and see them in her office at all hours of day or night, weekends or holidays, for sometimes no other reason than to put the parents at ease. And the parents were an interesting cross section of society. As word of her competence and compassion spread, she came to take care of a representative slice of East Coast society. From the dirt poor to the embarrassingly wealthy; from the neighbors next door to representatives of state government. Being in practice in north-eastern New Jersey, she also had the dubious pleasure of taking care of a number of children belonging to members of organized crime syndicates.

"Mother", I would bemoan; "these people steal, embezzle, corrupt and kill for a living! How can you accept them as patients?";

"I do not care what parents do. I take care of children, and they are always the innocents", was the response, in her thick Middle Eastern accent which she never lost, even after 60 years.

---

[1] Patients in this sense means the families. Her actual patients, the children, loved her for reasons I never completely understood, but glimpsed when I saw her kneeling on the floor to talk and embrace them. As a result, during a practice spanning 45 years and many thousands of patients, not once did she have to deal with a medical malpractice suit.

[2] The children – healthy, sick, suffering, or dying – were never a burden. But their parents, and especially the mothers, were unbelievably demanding. I actually considered Pediatrics as a career, but quickly learned that I had neither the patience nor the innate skills to deal with the families.

In her era, it was acceptable for physicians to receive gifts from grateful patients. And in turn, my mother would reach out and help her patients in times of need. She wrote off overdue bills that would make an accountant clutch his heart, bought winter jackets, gloves and shoes for her wanting patients, and I know of one instance when she contributed to the educational camp of one of her pediatric patients.

My mother thought nothing of these acts, comparing them to favors you do for family, for that was how she saw the children. These are behaviors that today would result in a collective gasp and an investigation by the state Medical Board, followed swiftly by censure and possible loss of license. My mother would scoff at accusations of favoritism or indebtedness, and point to the fact that she continues to receive calls of gratitude, well-wishing cards, and occasional visits from the parents and her grown-up patients, 25 years after her retirement. Modern Medical Boards and supervisory bodies believe they are keeping the profession honorable, but I can't help but feel that somewhere, in some soon to be forgotten corner, we've lost something warm and caring and special along the path.

* * *

When people would inquire and find out that both of my parents were physician, they immediately make the assumption that my career choice was inevitable, but I'm not sure that is valid. I am the only physician out of the pool of her children and grandchildren[1]. And even if the predictions turned out to be accurate, that fact eluded me for a decade out

---

[1] The career choices of her great-grandchildren remain to be seen.

of high school. I always had a variety of interests, and I chose this period in my life to sample them.

So, while many of my classmates pursued professional careers out of high school, and some chose the medical field and were well on their way to establishing themselves, I dropped out of college after two years of mediocre grades and chased a career in aviation, then computers & electronics, and even dabbled in setting up a business. But apparently the calling was always there, because after the birth of my son I decided enough was enough, and went back to finish my college degree and apply to medical school.

The Beginning

The road to becoming a physician is rather long and arduous, and defines the expression 'delayed gratification'. For most students with advanced education, high school is followed by college - four years for a graduate degree, or two years or less for an associate degree. At this point most of the graduates begin work in their careers, and settle down.

For the aspiring physician, following the four-year college graduate degree comes the competitive application to medical school, and typically another four years. At graduation, one is awarded a Medical Doctorate degree, and the initials 'M.D.' magically appear after your name and everyone calls you 'Doctor', especially your proud mother. But you're not there yet. You can't treat, you can't prescribe, you better not operate, and you really are not in the position of giving medical advice, since all your training is academic. You know the shoulder rotator cuff is made up of four muscles, and not only can you name them in your sleep, but you can also induce yawning in any layperson by also describing their nerves and blood supply. But why your grandfather's shoulder hurts is as much a mystery to the newly minted Doctor as it is to the prospective patient.

Hopefully by this point you know in what direction and which specialty your interests lie. There then follows another four years of medical education, called 'Internship' in the first year, and 'Residency' for the remainder. These are archaic terms from an era when physicians in training basically resided at the hospital, behind locked doors, until deemed competent enough to be safely released into the real world.

If your interest is in the surgical specialties, you're looking at another two to three years of surgical training after your residency, or six to seven years total after medical school.

And of course, if you're interest is in the more focused specialties, then you have another two to four years to go, slaving crazy hours doing the dirty work for others who have already paid their dues.

So, while your friends find their niches in life, settle down with their careers and families, and look towards building their nest eggs, you're still essentially a student. Titled, respected in social circles, proudly held up by your mother as an example to your younger siblings, but a student nonetheless.

For this and many other reasons, medicine remains a calling. I've known a few resident physicians who were in it for the money, a few more who were in it for the social prestige, but for the vast majority, slogging thru the hours, the bed pans, the smelly infected skin sores, the mean and ungrateful drunken patients, and the vicious, vindictive supervisory nurses, it is truly a calling. And nothing is better in the world than getting up every day knowing you are answering your calling in life. And the income and the prestige are simply added icing on a very nice cake.

I knew very early in my medical training that I wanted to be an Obstetrician and Gynecologist. The combination of healthy patients, happy outcomes, and the opportunity for developing and utilizing surgical skills were simply irresistible. Unfortunately, it took me a decade out of high school to make this determination, so I started a bit behind my peers. The advantage gained was I had a much more extensive life experience, and I had left many of my immaturities behind. And by that point in my life, I was focused and driven.

Starting with my second year of medical education I attended a facility based in the center of Newark, New Jersey. While I had to deal with potential muggings every day, and my vehicle was vandalized a couple of times, the experiences I gained in human interactions and the depth of depravity were priceless. As part of my training, in my third and fourth year of attendance I was given the choice of a month-long elective rotation with a team of residents, in order to pick up first-hand experience. I chose trauma surgery initially, and enjoyed it so much that I made the same choice the following year. In those decades (early 1980's) HIV was just beginning to rear its ugly head, and the extensive use of guns to settle trivial disagreements had not yet become commonplace. We did have a significant Puerto Rican population in the area served by the medical school, and they turned out to have a fondness for knives and machetes as a means of making a point and settling differences. As a result, I saw a number of interesting demonstrations of the consequence of stopping a swinging heavy sharp blade with various parts of the anatomy; usually the extremities, but occasionally head, neck and body. I also received first-hand knowledge of the results of high-speed deceleration upon the body, usually from being an occupant during a car accident, occasionally involving a motorcycle, and a few times from the consequences of falls after jumping or being pushed off of a building. And rarely, for variety, the result of interaction with a high-speed projectile. Shootings in those days were significantly different[1]. To make a point, the victim was shot in the extremities or abdomen, and occasionally, to really emphasize the point, the genitals or buttocks. To permanently end an argument, the target was the chest. Head shots were rare, unlike today.

---

[1]The most extreme case today is "C-Spining". The victim is shot at close range in the back of the neck, the intent being not to kill, but to sever the spinal column and render permanent paralysis from the neck down, sometimes necessitating life on a ventilator.

Inner City Dentistry

The area of Newark where the clinic and hospital were located had a large population of street workers, usually female, and readily identified by the absence of upper and lower incisors. It quickly became apparent that their primary employment managers (commonly labeled 'pimps') would introduce them to the trade by knocking out their front teeth, thereby improving, expediting and increasing the profitability of the act of oral sex. Most of the girls had drug abuse issues as well, and it was commonly understood that their pimps encouraged the abuse and addiction as a means of control. Some of the girls were unbelievably young, some of them unbelievably beautiful, even thru the grime and dirt and attitude, and almost all of them had a history of physical and sexual abuse or abandonment as children. As a result, they were all hardened, wary, skeptical, incredibly street smart, and resigned to their lifestyle. I soon learned that I had neither the skills nor the training for intervention, that the only thing I could hope to accomplish was to treat their frequent sexually transmitted infections, encourage continuation of contraception, tend the cuts, bruises and broken ribs and split lips and swollen faces, and be ready to listen when they had the need to share their pain. And oh, ever so rarely, to be ready to refer to available agencies when one was ready to look beyond the next day, the next meal, the next fix, the next rape, or the next brutal beating.

And sometimes when it was too late for anything, all one could do was sadly think of the possibilities that could have been, the future that never was, and the young life that was prematurely brought to a violent and senseless end.

During my rotation thru surgical trauma, I vividly recall the day I was offered the opportunity to practice suturing by closing multiple knife stab wounds. The victim was dead, the police finished with their cursory investigation, and I had about 20 or so one-inch cuts to practice closing. And then I noticed the person, or rather the person that was. She was young, in her mid-20's, mixed race with beautiful skin tone even in death, delicate features, and eyes of an unusual shade of green. Beautiful, perfect pearly white teeth, although of course she was missing the front upper and lower incisors. She had been stabbed repeatedly in the chest and abdomen, with the wounds clustered around her breasts. And as I closed one stab wound after another, I suddenly realized that she had been stabbed with a steak knife, for some of the wounds had been made with the blade at an angle to the skin, and as a result there was the scalloping pattern of the blade edge on the skin. And in my mind, I pictured the beautiful young woman pleading and screaming in helpless agony as the assailant repeatedly forced the blade of the steak knife into her chest. And the recurring thought, the pain, and the imagined sound and feel of the steel penetrating the flesh led to nausea, a rush for the bathroom, and the only time I have ever gotten sick over the state of flesh or the sight of blood.

And all of it was a priceless experience for a physician in training.

We were exposed to many acts of violence, man on man, man on woman, man upon man, and rarely, woman upon man.

One of my first cases in trauma surgery was a man and woman who had been the victims of a machete attack. It came to light that they were in bed, engaged in or planning a more amorous interaction, when the proclaimed true partner of the woman walked onto the scene. How he came to be in possession of a machete at that moment was never explained, but I suspect he walked in with some pre-knowledge of the situation. He attacked his competition first by swinging the blade down, while the victim raised his arm at the same moment in a defensive gesture. The blade connected in-between the third and fourth finger, and its momentum led to separation of the bones of the hand, the wrist, and even partially separated the two bones of the forearm. When brought in to the emergency room he was suffering from a surprisingly small amount of blood loss, but his arm resembled, if nothing else, a crab claw. He underwent a surprisingly complete repair, and after healing the only significant permanent loss he suffered was reduced wrist mobility. One could only hope that he also gained a new level of respect for jealousy.

The woman in the situation did not escape unscathed, for the angry and scorned lover next turned his attention to her, and swung at her face with the blade. The blade landed vertically about the middle of her face and, meeting bone resistance, slid off to one side, peeling off most of the soft tissues with it. She in turn presented to the emergency room as a grotesque harlequin caricature, for from one side her face looked normal, even attractive; from the other side there was a bloody mass of raw tissue and hair hanging off, revealing much of her facial bones, and her teeth all the way back to her molars. Her repair took somewhat longer, and the results were not what one would call satisfactory. I suspect her future dating pictures always showed her face from the same profile.

* * *

A gentleman in his mid-40's was brought in one night following a significant motor vehicle accident. He was rather large, loud, and somewhat bruised, but did not appear to have suffered terribly, and without evidence of any bone fractures or head trauma. He also had a poor command of English, and kept muttering regularly, and yelling occasionally, in a language that no one could understand. Evaluation by the Medical Technicians enroute had revealed stable vital signs, heart function was normal, and he was on a gurney in the emergency room awaiting x-ray evaluation on a rather busy night.

He was, however somewhat obnoxious and belligerent, and kept wanting to get up. The nursing staff, assuming intoxication, kept pushing him back down ever more forcefully, and yelling and cursing at him repeatedly. If someone is continuously uncooperative, they obviously have no significant traumatic issues or injuries.

Finally, due to his continued uncooperative behavior, the busy and impatient nursing staff resorted to restraints[1].

Now, with his arms and legs tied down to the gurney, the gentleman became even more belligerent, thrashing about, yelling and jabbering continuously, and amazingly still struggling to get up. Just as the patience of the staff was reaching its limits, he began to quiet down, and finally passed out[2]. Vital signs were once again checked, and this time revealed complete heart failure.

Suddenly the patient that everyone hoped would go away became the center of attention in the emergency room. A cardiac arrest code was called, resuscitation efforts were undertaken, and appropriate medications administered, and blood in anticipation of transfusion was ordered.

All to no avail.

The entire episode, from arrival to the cessation of efforts at resuscitation and declaring the patient deceased, had taken less than three hours.

---

[1] Today, the use of restraints is much more regulated and restricted.
[2] Sedation is generally avoided in cases of trauma, at least until head injury has been completely ruled out.

The autopsy revealed a hip fracture, which happened to cross a major pelvic artery and resulted in a tear. He was suffering from terrible pain, both from the undiagnosed fracture and the pressure of the large volume of blood pooling in his pelvis. He eventually bled out internally. He was not intoxicated, he wasn't a bad person, and suddenly, far too late for any atonement, the source of his uncooperative and belligerent behavior became clear.

I watched as his wife arrived in short order with a small child in tow. Her command of the English language was even less than his, but her sobs and wails left no doubt as to depth of her grief, nor any need for a translator.

To have died unnecessarily in his mid-40's, leaving a widow and a child without a father and provider, was bad enough. What really stayed with me was knowing that he had died following terrible and progressive suffering, in a modern hospital with an advanced trauma unit and all the expertise and equipment necessary to help him. The language barrier left him unable to make a point with the medical staff surrounding him, and while being treated casually and disrespectfully, he was restrained in his final hour of utter misery.

At that moment, I swore that I would never prejudge, and would listen and attend to any patient, no matter how unpleasant, at least until I understood their situation.

My resolve was at times severely tested, but it was one promise I really worked hard at keeping.

There was the gentleman who after a night of depressive drinking at a bar went into his car and decided to end it all by using a handy, loaded shotgun. Placing the barrel under his chin, he neglected to use the 'toe in the trigger' technique. As a result, while stretching to reach the trigger, he tilted his head back. When he finally succeeded in his endeavor the blast removed most of his lower jaw, the middle of his upper jaw, and created an inverted V-shaped trench stretching from the base of where his nose once resided, to his forehead. His skull was not penetrated, his brain uninjured beyond what was inflicted by years of drinking and self-neglect, and he was brought into the trauma center alive, breathing, unrecognizable, and semi-conscious. The trauma team worked hours to stabilize him, while the plastic surgery department spent months restoring his features, and an admirable job at that, considering the degree of destruction. But, with his depressive existence made worse by the scarring and distortions of his face, all involved in his care and recovery were rewarded by his second and successful suicide attempt a couple of years later. I never found out if it was the same shotgun.

* * *

Suicide is a subject close to home, since my father, a struggling general surgeon, successfully hung himself on New Year's Day in 1977[1]. And while women attempt suicide at far greater rates than men, the more lethal forms chosen by men result in more success overall.

Some of the most unfortunate cases involved failed attempts.

A young man, depressed over a recently broken relationship, decided it was easier to end the pain by using a borrowed handgun. He placed the barrel against his temple, in front of his ear, and pulled the trigger. Fortunately, or unfortunately, depending on an individual's perspective,

---

[1] Since that day I have found out that surgeons and anesthesiologists have some of the highest suicide rates amongst professionals, to the degree that it is an identified job hazard.

moving from one side to the other at that point puts the path of the bullet outside of the brain cavity, his presumed target. It does however cross both optic nerves, the main nerve bundle connecting the visual part of the eyeball to the brain. So, in one brief instant, he managed to create a small, round opening on one side of his face, a large defect on the other (where the bullet exited and blew out part of his face) and totally blinded himself. Hopefully his next attempt was tempered by his inability to see the result of the first attempt, and hampered by his inability to locate the proper tool.

* * *

Bullets do funny things when they interact with flesh and bone. Another interesting trauma case involved the victim of an attempted execution. He was laying on the floor, looking up at his standing assailant, who pointed the barrel of a 32-caliber revolver at his forehead and pulled the trigger. The bullet entered the skin of the forehead at the intended site, but instead of penetrating the skull, the bullet flattened to the size of a 25-cent piece, then traveled along the curve of the skull underneath the scalp, and came out the back thru a large hole, again in the scalp. The concussion knocked the victim unconscious, the hole in the forehead and the one in the back gushed blood, and the combination no doubt led the assailant to congratulate himself on a job well done, and he walked away without further investigation or attempts. The victim was awake by the time the squad brought him into the emergency room, the bleeding controlled with pressure dressings, and he went home a day later, uncooperative with the police, since I suspect he planned his own form of justice. I never found out if he succeeded, or if he went back, retrieved, and kept the flattened bullet as a good luck talisman.

Given his lifestyle, the latter I would have highly recommended.

The magic performed by the trauma team was something to behold. Cases that I would have thought were beyond help, begging for last rites were miraculously brought back to life. Damage to flesh and bone that strained imagination and defied description were methodically cleaned, re-arranged, and made whole again.

And then there were the distractions.

While covering the trauma unit one very quiet night, exhausted from continuously attending to cases during the day, we received a call that a late-term pregnant patient was being transported into the emergency room. She was described as having trauma to the abdomen, via a large knife, with arrival estimated in ten minutes. Suddenly wide awake, I sat right up with excitement, as this was a perfect opportunity for application of my skills. The squad meanwhile provided a surprising lack of details, only that vitals were not available enroute. Even more exciting: stab wounds to a pregnant abdomen with a likely perimortem cesarean, forgetting in the excitement of the moment that my educational opportunity may have come at the price of the life of a young woman in the late stages of her pregnancy. I had been in an exhausted sleep in the call room near the end of my 24-hour shift, but now I stood in anticipation, adrenalin pumping and hands shaking with a combination of excitement and fear. My brain was a maelstrom of thoughts while reviewing the necessary steps in the remaining few minutes before the lifeless patient was wheeled into our unit, and we proceeded with our heroic measures to save the baby.

And before I knew it, or felt remotely ready, the time was up, and the gurney was wheeled into the Emergency Room.

And what is this?

Under restraints on the gurney was a large woman, made significantly larger by her ample pregnant belly. But instead of lying lifeless and pale and covered with blood, she was beet red, straining against the leather restraining straps, and screaming obscenities at the top of her voice, and spraying a fountain of spittle, directed at anyone within her visual range. Turned out the "knife trauma to the belly" involved being struck by the handle of the knife, and the "lack of vitals enroute" was due to the patient's refusal to cooperate with the Emergency Technicians. She was physically fine, although rip-roaring drunk at near the end of her pregnancy. She was shortly sedated and quiet, briefly questioned by the police and dismissed in the morning. I was not able to sleep anymore the rest of that otherwise very quiet evening.

And all of it was a priceless experience for a physician in training.

* * *

During my training I was amazed at the abuses and neglect that the human body can absorb and endure and still continue to function. It is truly a testament to the built-in reserves and recovery capabilities. Some of the most extreme examples were seen in intravenous drug abusers, and in central Newark the predominant drug of the day was heroin. Shortly, crack cocaine would take the number one spot, followed by the incredibly addictive methamphetamine in its various forms. And this being the 1980's, HIV-AIDS had already begun to rear its ugly head, but the drug community remained frighteningly complacent, and the desperation for the next fix resulted in some bizarre behavior.

First the addict has to obtain the drug. The street girls were amply supplied by their pimps, who would occasionally withhold the drug as a very effective form of punishment. For the rest, the usual source was the friendly local supplier. To increase profits and lower cost to the user, the street form of the drug was diluted, or cut, by an unbelievable mixture of substances. Some known examples were Bisquick, baking soda, talcum powder, powdered milk and even laundry detergent. One consequence of the repeated dilution was that at any given time the actual potency of the drug mixture was unknown.

To dissolve the heroin, which is usually obtained in powder form, one needs water, a holder, a source of heat, and depending on the mixture, some form of acidic fluid. Also requisite is a tourniquet, a syringe, and a quiet place to carry out the deed. In our locale, the quiet place chosen was frequently a bathroom stall[1]. It provided privacy and a source of water, namely the toilet bowl. The holder was frequently a spoon, the heater a butane lighter or match, and for the tourniquet a couple of condoms tied together. For the acidic fluid, a drop or two of lemon juice or vinegar would suffice.

Given the location, the contamination, and the nasty additives present in the street level cuts of the drug, the addicts would end up injecting not only the narcotic, but also a witch's brew of bacteria and unknown chemicals and substances. This resulted in some interesting consequences. First up was the infection at the site of injection, which involved the skin (in the form of a large boil filled with pus) and the vein. The scarring of the latter usually meant that the site could only be used once or twice before it completely scarred and collapsed, necessitating use of another site.

---

[1] On two separate occasions, addicts that had died from overdosing were found, still sitting on the public bathroom stall at the hospital, after injecting. In one case, the young addict was bent over while sitting, the tourniquet was still tight with the needle still in the vein.

Eventually all of the veins accessible to the addict's dominant arm will have collapsed, and they will have to switch to the non-dominant arm, which means the injection sites are less precise and more haphazard.

And all too soon, no easily accessible sites remain.

But the need for continuing injections is still present. Options at this point however, are limited. If the user has access to funds, they can seek out a site where a skilled individual can be found to thread the carotid vein in the neck and inject the drugs, hopefully with some semblance of cleanliness. In the parlance of the trade, this is referred to as 'mainlining'.

For the rest, the option to 'skin pop' was the way to go.

The typical skin popper has in their possession the liquefied compound in a syringe with a needle. The drug is injected under the skin, raising a bleb, and the absorption leads to the high. Unfortunately, the absorption is slow, and to get the necessary rush, multiple skin injections are made, sometimes on the order of up to a half dozen or more. Given the dirty technique and material, each site will usually get infected, produce a large pus-filled boil progressing to an ulcer, before resolving over a period of days to a week or longer. And in the meantime, the user is skin popping daily. The net result is dozens and dozens of infected skin sites in various stages of scarring and healing.

As a result, the constant inflammation and the body's production of protective proteins leads to a condition called amyloidosis. The overproduction of these inflammatory proteins, designed to protect the body under normal circumstances, overwhelms the associated recycling mechanisms. Not being cleared, the proteins end up getting deposited in various organs, typically causing stiffness and rigidity in the heart (an organ that functions best when flexible and mobile), the liver (interfering with its myriad complex and critical functions), and the brain (an organ that doesn't appreciate deposition of any foreign substance).

And so, while the heart struggles to move the blood and the liver struggles to keep it clean, the brain becomes more befuddled. But thru it all the addiction and self-abuse continue.

I can count on one hand the number of young street addicts that I observed overcoming the call of the dragon and succeeding in getting their lives back into a semblance of normality. The degree of physical recovery in those that succeeded was truly breathtaking.

And all of it was a priceless experience for a physician in training.

Crabs and Late-Night Meals

In my third year of Residency training, I was unexpectedly offered a chance to volunteer at an inner-city clinic offering free and no-questions-asked screening for sexually transmitted infections (STI). Describing it as volunteering is a bit misleading, for the clinic paid $20 per hour to working residents, a windfall at the time. The clinic was funded by the county government and was primarily geared to serving the paid sex workers of the city, but was open to anyone on a walk-in basis. As crazy as my schedule was during training, I jumped at the opportunity. It turned out to be another insightful lesson in humanity and human behavior.

Choosing to work on Thursday nights, in a very short time I became acquainted with the night ladies of downtown Omaha, who preferred to be examined before the weekend rush[1]. One thinks of working girls as human trafficking victims or substance abusers who are in turn abused by pimps and johns, and are desperately seeking an opportunity to escape their circumstances. The girls that I met while working at the STI clinic were mostly open about what they did, and acceptant of their life and profession. They readily joked and shared stories about recent experiences, and expressed surprising level of gratification with their lifestyle. Their only universal concern was the police department's vice squad. I'm sure that there were dark circumstances behind their façade, but in a limited time slot, while examining them for the latest infection, I

---

[1] There was a marked difference in my impression of the working girls in downtown Omaha, Nebraska, and the ones I met during my training in downtown Newark, New Jersey. I had the opportunity to spend more productive time interacting with the former, who were being seen during voluntary health checks, versus the latter who were in the trauma unit. I was also better trained and more perceptive and comfortable interacting by this point in my career. And yes, there were working young men also, but my training primarily limited me to the females.

never had the time to delve into the details of their lives. I did get to know a number of them, and they in turn accepted me into their circle of trusted acquaintances. One of the consequences of the latter came to light when I was chosen to take three Residency candidates out to dinner, downtown, on a Friday night. I made a wrong turn, proceeded down a one-way street, and ended up in the seedier section of downtown Omaha. I was soon crimson red and blubbering an explanation, for upon turning the last corner I was instantly recognized and warmly greeted by hand waves, and called out on a first name basis by a group of idle and obvious ladies of the night. My clumsy attempts at explanation only seemed to make the matter worse, much to the amusement of my passengers. I took extra precautions to avoid that area in the future.

* * *

The rules of the clinic were rather simple. Each patient was seen in a fifteen minute slot, after their brief history and chief complaints were noted by the admitting staff. They were also asked their name, but no identification was required. If the individual were female, I performed a vaginal exam and obtained cultures[1], and based upon their symptoms and very loose criteria, provided a treatment for the most common community acquired sexually transmitted infection[2].

---

[1] The cultures took three to four days, and were done to maintain statistics for the state. The patients were all treated presumptively.

[2] When one thinks of sexually transmitted infection, usually Gonorrhea or Chlamydia or HIV come to mind. The astute may include Herpes or genital warts (the most common STI in the US). There are a number of other sexually transmitted infections, mild to severe, and considered exotic by the medical community in the United States. There's also a distinction between an infection (microbes that invade cells and cause symptoms), and infestations (usually caused by critters that live on, or just below, the skin surface).

If the patient were male and a discharge was present, I again obtained a culture, but also performed a slide examination, having collected a drop on a slide, and using a clinic microscope that was a direct descendent of the one I recalled using in my high school biology class. The patient was again treated rather indiscriminately.

One pattern quickly emerged.

Males with Gonorrhea develop a profuse, green-yellow discharge from the penis. I won't try to quantify it, but the discharge is so copious that the patient will inevitably insert something into their underwear to absorb it, or at least keep it in check and out of their pants and socks until the next underwear change. And the most readily available and cheapest absorbent is a wad of toilet paper.

And so it came to pass that the presenting symptom of Gonorrhea in males was the 'toilet paper sign' – a wad of toilet tissue, stuffed in the underwear, and streaked, stained, sticky, and at times saturated with the aforementioned greenish-yellow discharge. The discharge itself and the subsequent examination under the microscope were simply the technical confirmation. The patients' presenting complaint was often comical, for they would innocently confess to having "a bit of a discharge", while standing with their rather obvious and saturated toilet paper sign.

* * *

One of my more memorable patients at the clinic was a lady, who was introduced by the nurse as Jane, with a complaint of a recent onset of some genital itching. She immediately stood out from the usual clinic crowd, standing tall and erect, quite attractive in her 40's, while sporting designer purse and shoes, and speaking in cultured tones. She also maintained direct eye contact during our brief introduction, which was unusual on the first visit. The opulent ring on her finger clarified her marital status, and her anonymous presence at an inner-city STI clinic wordlessly spoke volumes of her indiscretions. I did my usual inquiries while she prepared herself. Nothing very dramatic, until I lifted her gown and focused my light. On closer examination, her pubic region appeared to be slowly undulating, and the source of the movement were innumerable tiny, pale insects moving between and upon the hair shafts.

Recent onset of some genital itching, indeed!

This was by far the worst case of pubic lice I had ever witnessed or read about in any text, or heard described by any clinician. Resisting the urge to squeal, jump back, and run out of the room, I went thru my routine of doing a vaginal examination and obtaining cultures, perhaps a bit quicker and at longer arm's length than usual[1]. The nurse and I quickly left the room following the exam and cleaned up multiple times.

After the patient was dressed, I explained to her that we did not stock the normal medication for her condition. She understood that I would have to give her a prescription, preferably under her real name, but no one else needed to be the wiser. For the first time she lowered her eyes and gave me a full name. I'd like to think that her husband was the rascal in the relationship, but her presence at our clinic made that unlikely. I also hoped that she was able to successfully delouse herself, her clothes, her linen, her laundry, her bed, her house, her car, and her pets without her husband being the wiser. If nothing else I hoped that in the future she

---

[1] It was a psychological effect. Pubic lice are not easily acquired with casual contact, especially by someone wearing gloves, hence their common designation as sexually transmitted.

would be a bit more discriminatory in her liaisons. Thirty years later I still find myself scratching needlessly just thinking about her.

* * *

Since my STI clinic hours typically ran from seven to ten PM, I had to rush over from the hospital after rounds, and then make my way home after finishing the clinic paperwork. Dinner was a lost cause on these nights, so after leaving the clinic I often stopped to grab a quick bite at a national fast-food chain drive-thru around the corner. I knew it was an unhealthy habit, but by the time I got home it was too late to look for something to eat. It was a very unhealthy habit that fortuitously eliminated itself one night.

This particular evening was unremarkable, until the last patient. A male complaining of some penile discharge. He was brought into the exam room wearing the very distinctive uniform of an employee of my dinner drive-thru fast-food chain. I was sitting on the exam stool, while he was standing facing me, and I asked him to lower his pants and underwear so I could perform an exam. It became immediately obvious that he was presenting with the 'toilet paper sign'. He casually removed the partially saturated wad with his bare hand and tossed it in the nearby bin, while I cringed. I obtained a swab culture, and then asked him to produce a drop in the middle of the slide that I was holding. Most males at this point proceed with a milking action, which produces an ample drop the first time. This gentleman proceeded with a thumb and forefinger rapid stroking motion which resulted in his penis whipping side to side, and numerous flying droplets of penile discharge in all directions. I undoubtedly squealed, for he ceased about the same time I jumped back. I had the drop on my slide, and probably much more than I expected or cared to think about. The gentleman at this time pulled everything back up and proceeded to wipe his recently occupied hand on his work uniform.

"I'll be right back" I called as I quickly walked out, went directly to the work station, and proceed to vigorously wash everything that was washable in the small clinic sink. Examination of the slide revealed no surprises.

I went back, and gave him the usual end of exam talk, with a diagnosis, medications, and precautions.

As he prepared to take his leave, I found myself fearfully confirming my suspicions.

"So where do you work?", I asked, hoping the answer was across the river in Iowa.

"Around the corner", was his reply.

"What do you do?"

Please dear Lord, let him be the janitor.

"I'm the cook", he replied.

Could it possibly get any worse?

"So, are you done for the night?", I fearfully asked.

"No", he answered; "I'm on break and have to get back".

As I said, it was an unhealthy habit that fortuitously took care of itself.

Gynecology

The root of the word Gynecology derives from the Greek Gyne- (women or female) and French -logie (study of). It defines the branch of medicine dealing with the health care of women, especially the diagnosis and treatment of disorders affecting the female reproductive system[1]. Other interesting words with the Gyne- root include Gynecocracy (political supremacy of women), Gynecocratic (society or government ruled by women), Misogyny (hatred of women) and Monogyny (practice of having one wife).

And why do women need their own medical specialist? Mainly due to the complexity of the female reproductive system, and the myriad issues, abnormalities and dysfunctions that can arise.

The word Gynecologist was coined in the 17th Century, but even without direct evidence, there is little doubt that specialists tending to the care of women preceded written history. This care, outside of pregnancy, involved problems having to do with menstruation, failure of conception, tumors, and infections, among other issues[2].

* * *

One of the oldest infections of the reproductive system involves sexually transmitted infections, or STI's. In the United States the top five, in order

---

[1] The male equivalent would be an Andrologist, but of course there is no such specialty. The male reproductive organs include the testicles, prostate, penis, and their interconnecting ducts. Most issues in the male are addressed by Urologists or Proctologists, who also address problems in women, making them non-gender specific.

[2] Another interesting issue was the responsibility for the gender of babies. It's amazing how long it took society to stop blaming women for selecting the wrong gender for their newborns. Anne Boleyn, wife of Henry the 8th, was executed because he demanded a son, and she gave birth to a daughter instead. Far from being a rarity, she was only the most famous example.

of prevalence, are genital warts (caused by Human Papilloma Virus, or HPV), Herpes (caused by the Herpes simplex virus, or HSV), Chlamydia (caused by Chlamydia trachomatis, a primitive bacteria), HIV-AIDS (caused by the Human Immunodeficiency Virus), and Gonorrhea (caused by Neisseria gonorrhoeae, a bacteria). Trichomoniasis, a genital infection caused by a parasite, would be number two on this list, but the only reason it's not included is that there is some evidence that it can be spread by non-sexual contact (similar to pubic lice), and about three out of four infected individuals, male or female, are symptom free. Untreated, it will often clear over a period of months, although it can increase the risk of getting other sexually transmitted infections, and is associated with preterm labor in the pregnant woman. The primary presenting complaint in women with Trichomoniasis is vaginal itching and a thin, odorous discharge.

Genital warts are surprisingly common. Before the advent of the associated vaccine, about 70-80% of sexually active adults had evidence of exposure. The infection can vary from complete lack of symptoms to extensive external or internal warts, but fortunately in most people it is self-limiting. A few subtypes are associated with cancer – cervical in women, and penile in men. It is the most common cause of cervical cancer in reproductive age women worldwide. Other subtypes of the virus cause warts that can be flat or flower like, growing out from a narrow base. The former often present as small bumps on the genital skin; the latter occasionally can cause massive overgrowth of a cauliflower-like lesion, extending three to four inches or more above the skin[1]. The disease has an

---

[1] One gentleman that I examined at the STI clinic had a large, irregular, circumferential growth, about half an inch thick, around the base of the glans – the head of the penis. Given options for treatment, he firmly declined. It seems his sexual partner enjoyed the extra stimulation provided by the growth during

unpredictable course, no doubt due to the many sub-types of the virus. Most visible infections present as small lumps on the skin, usually smooth, but sometimes with a cauliflower-like appearance[1]. Many women are asymptomatic after infection, either because the presentation doesn't draw attention, or the site of the infection is internal. Most patients, even the ones with visible lesions, will clear the virus after a period of months to years. In some women, the warts continue to spread, either thru repeated sexual activity, or by local spread, or because their immune system cannot handle the challenge. At times, these cases can become quite dramatic. I recall a patient with extensive internal warts, covering the top of the vagina and the entire surface of the cervix. I tried burning the lesions with a guided laser, but during her follow-up visit, it seemed the lesions had reestablished themselves. At the time, I could only offer her a referral to an educational institution where experimental immune therapies were undergoing trials. Unfortunately, I never saw her back, so I do not know the degree of success or failure.

In some patients, the virus seems to alter the cellular machinery in such a way that pre-cancerous, and eventually cancerous changes take place. These alterations can occur on the external genitals, the walls of the vagina, or most commonly, the cervix. HPV is the only clearly identified virus that can cause malignancy in otherwise normal tissue[2]. One solution came about with approval of the HPV vaccine in 2006.

---

intercourse. I reviewed the infectious nature of the lesion, and dropped the matter at that point, knowing that human sexuality knows no bounds.

[1] See Plates 15-17.

[2] There is strong evidence linking H. pylori – a bacteria that causes common heartburn and ulcers – to stomach cancer. But the link appears to be thru persistent inflammation and not a direct alteration of cellular DNA.

Herpes is a persistent infection caused by a virus related to Chicken Pox. One gets infected by skin contact with someone who is shedding the virus. There actually needs to be a break in the skin for the virus to enter and get a toehold, but it doesn't take much. Sexual activity often creates small abrasions which are enough to allow entry. Once established, the virus becomes entrenched, as there have been very few cases of a confirmed infection actually clearing out, although in many patients the manifestations of the infection may only occur once. Testing however, will reveal the virus to be lying dormant, and if the immune system is weakened by any significant factor, it can reappear[1]. The virus tends to stay at the site of the initial exposure, as it infects the nerve bundles serving that area. The initial infection can be quite nasty, with multiple blisters and significant pain. Recurrences tend to be milder, and are usually heralded by tingling or numbness in the relevant area. While the virus is copiously present during each recurrence, the body can shed viral particles from the infected area even in the absence of lesions or symptoms. The good news is that there are a number of approved medications that help to keep the virus suppressed, and work continues on developing an effective, preventative vaccine.

* * *

Chlamydia and Gonorrhea can both cause devastating infections in women, frequently resulting in infertility if left untreated. Gonorrhea is notorious for spreading via the Fallopian tubes into the abdominal cavity and causing extensive scarring, and even peritonitis, a widespread and potentially deadly infection of the abdomen. Another route of spread is up the ureters, the tubes that drain the kidneys into the bladder. The

---

[1] Factors include other illnesses, persistent stress, nutritional deficiency, and age, just to name some examples.

infection causes scarring and copious pus production which can cause blockage and result in back flow of the urine, an incredibly painful experience. Exactly how painful is demonstrated by an entry in a clinical textbook from the 1700's, and I quote:

> "The individual was bent double over a support in the courtyard, at high noon, for adequate illumination. Her urethra[1] was dilated with a funnel, allowing visualization of the opening of the ureters[2]. A wire was passed up the ureter on the blocked side, until resistance was felt. Multiple attempts at further passage were finally met with a sudden loss of resistance, followed shortly by a large gush of urine and pus into the bladder, and a sigh of relief from the grateful patient."

How awful the pain that after this unimaginable torture in a courtyard at high noon, the grateful patient responded with a "sigh of relief".

* * *

Multiple volumes can be written on the other sexually transmitted infections. For unknown reasons Syphilis appears to be making a comeback in the United States, and there are alarming increases in cases of antibiotic resistant Gonorrhea around the world. Where once the infection could be cured with a short course of oral antibiotics, some cases now require intravenous combination of medications over many days.

One shudders at the thought of where we are headed if present trends continue.

---

[1] Tube leading from the bladder to the outside.
[2] Tubes leading from the kidneys into the bladder.

Circumcisions and other mutilations

In the age of medicine in the not-too-distant future, some of the procedures carried out today will be looked upon as barbaric by our descendants, just as we judge many of the procedures from the past. One example of a procedure that will surely come to pass involves circumcision of the male infant[1].

* * *

Male circumcision is practiced by a number of cultures. The origin is hidden in antiquity, but some cultures practice it as a means of identification and unification with the group, some in a belief that it serves as a way to rise above animals, and others for hygienic reasons. And of course, the continuation into the modern age has much to do with tradition and identification with the father. On the positive side, there is good data that shows it significantly reduces the risk of acquiring certain sexually transmitted infections.

* * *

Then there is female circumcision[2].

This is a monstrously barbaric procedure that owes its origin in the belief that if women are allowed to enjoy intercourse, they will inevitably develop a wondering eye. And some anonymous man of religion[3],

---

[1] Circumcision. From the Latin 'circumcido', to cut around.

[2] Medically referred to as 'Female Genital Mutilation'.

[3] The origin is again lost in antiquity, but I have no doubt that men came up with the idea. I cannot imagine a woman deciding to proactively punish herself or her daughters with such a brutal act of mutilation.

somewhere in the distant past, determined that the best means of ensuring a woman's fidelity towards her husband was by destroying her anatomy. And what better time to accomplish this than at a young girl's arrival into puberty, when her eye will no doubt begin to gaze lustfully upon men. The procedure is usually done without the benefit of anesthesia or proper sanitation. The first time I examined a young lady who had undergone the total form of the procedure I found myself in shock and speechless. The mutilation of the external genitalia was complete and the scarring beyond description. I could not bring myself to insult the young lady further by asking her permission for a photograph.

* * *

If parents desire to circumcise their male newborn, I have no issues, and have in fact performed the procedure innumerable times on newborn males. But I would make certain that the young organ was properly and thoroughly anesthetized before proceeding. When I was first taught the procedure in my early Residency, my supervising staff physician assured me that no anesthetic was necessary since newborns do not feel pain. No one ever explained why, if the statement were true, did the baby scream loud enough to rattle windows and squirm so intensely during the procedure that the they had to be restrained or held down by an assistant, and parents were not allowed to watch. Over the decades the approach was gradually altered. First, the babies were given a cotton ball soaked in sugar water and held in their mouths via a gauze holder[1]. Later they were treated to a topical cream anesthetic that was applied for 10 minutes or so

---

[1] I never figured out if the babies were kept subdued by the presence of the sugar solution or by the choking effect of the cotton ball in the gauze carrier held in their mouths.

before the procedure, and finally, the organ was properly anesthetized with a local injection. They still cried during the injection, but it was hardly more than the cry associated with hunger. And so, the little ones were finally treated with the respect that was their due.

Although not intended as such, I do know of one sociological discussion that was settled fortuitously due to a circumcision.

* * *

The behavioral characteristics that differentiate little boys from little girls have raised arguments for generations[1].

Why do little boys tend to behave as little boys, while little girls tend to behave as little girls do? Is it some factor, some force, having to do with the presence or absence of that Y-chromosome? Do children behave the way society expects them to behave, or is it behavior associated or identified with the same-gender parent, or is there some innate biological difference among the genders?

Finally, is the gender associated behavior established while the fetus is developing in the uterus, from sex-chromosome factors and effects, or from observation of the parent and learned behavior, or from societal norms and expectations. This question has profound social implications, and while some answers may be gleaned from observation of non-traditional families or societies with different child rearing norms[2], there has never been a way to perform an ideal experiment.

---

[1] Yes, I'm fully aware that there are many exceptions. But I refer to generalities, the behavior of the different sexes as a group, rather than individuals.
[2] For example, some societies rear children as a group, with multiple care-takers, instead of individual family units.

Answering these questions is profoundly difficult. While most parents will allow their child to choose a play activity or groom at will, no parent will willingly allow their child to be forced into a role more commonly associated with the opposite sex, or not chosen by the child. And I can't imagine any parent, or ethics committee for that matter, allowing a male child to be given female hormones, or a female child to be given androgens, in order to test the effect of hormones on gender associated behavior.

* * *

And then on the 22nd of August, 1967, a perfect experiment presented itself.

That was the date when twin identical males were born in Canada, and shortly afterwards, during their circumcision, one of them suffered a penis injury severe enough that the organ was lost. Based on the recommendation of a prominent psychologist, with a track record of work in gender identity, it was decided to raise the injured child as a girl[1]. Surgically, it is much easier to convert the external genitals of a baby boy into that of a girl, rather than build up a new, functioning penis.

No doubt the desire of the psychologist to establish his theories and promote himself within the profession also played a role in the decision. And once the decision was made, all efforts were directed at maintaining the assignment.

---

[1] John Money. He no doubt saw an opportunity for fame & fortune, and support for his preferred point of view regarding gender identification. He published a number of studies on this case, until the poor outcome led to a humbling course reversal.

Thus, after the testes were removed, female hormones were administered, and surgery used to create a semblance of female external genitals and a vagina. The parents followed the advice of the professional, renamed, dressed and addressed the child as a girl, banned all male associated childhood activities for her, and allowed the experiment to proceed to puberty. The fact that the little girl struggled with her gender identity the entire time she was growing up did not seem to sway either the parents or the psychologist, and suggest that perhaps the wrong path had been taken[1].

The question of the origin of gender identity could not have had a better experiment designed for it, and the terrible turmoil that the child suffered, his voluntary reversion to a male at the end of puberty, and his mental anguish eventually leading to suicide should have settled the question. And yet we periodically still see gender assignment of babies born with undeveloped or ambiguous external genitalia based on convenience rather than medical fact.

---

[1] I refer the reader to *As Nature Made Him: The Boy Who Was Raised As A Girl,* by John Colapinto; Harper Perennial (2000).

The Cycle

Many women don't realize it, but they were born with their lifelong collection of potential eggs[1]. These take the form of quiescent follicles, and are the result of multiple levels of cell division and differentiation within the ovaries of the fetus in the second trimester. The actual number peaks around 24 weeks of uterine life, at around six million, but these cells begin dying off right away, and are down to around one to two million, give or take, at the time of birth[2].

At this point the newborn has quiet ovaries, and the primordial (primitive) follicles are dormant, and the girl continues to lose some regularly until the onset of puberty. With the center in the brain that controls the ovaries maturing around nine years of age, the stimulation of the follicles begins. First action is by the cells that surround the follicles within the ovaries. These cells are different from the rest of the ovary due to their physical proximity to the follicle, and they begin production and secretion of very low levels of Estrogen. The cumulative small amounts of Estrogen from thousands of these cells in turn begins the process of turning girls into women, by stimulating the development of the breasts, the changes in fat distribution that gives adult women their figures, the development of specialized hair follicles in the genital and underarm areas, the growth spurt, and within the brain the changes that seemingly overnight makes the obnoxiously immature guy next to you in class suddenly seem clever and funny.

---

[1] Males of course, produce sperm as the need arises.
[2] There is some evidence that some of the stem cells giving rise to future eggs are still present after birth and into adulthood, and continue to produce follicles, but the vast majority have done their job by the time the baby is born.

As the maturation of the brain center continues, a cyclic process begins. Unlike the common misconception, each cycle does not involve one follicle developing and releasing an egg. At the beginning of the cycle, dozens of follicles are recruited, and begin growing under the stimulus of hormones secreted by the brain. The follicles are really in a race, for as each follicle grows, its Estrogen secretion increases, and the follicle's receptors for the stimulating brain signal in turn increases. The overall increase in Estrogen however cranks down the stimulating signal (negative feedback) from the brain, and the drop in the signal causes the follicles to try and grab as much of the signal as they can. The lead follicle, the one with the most receptors, grabs most of the signal and in essence starves the remainder, which regress, die off and form a tiny scar within the ovary. This lead follicle is the one that is destined to release the egg around day 14 of the cycle. Once the egg is released, the remaining cells that surrounded the follicle continue to secrete Estrogen under brain stimulation for around 14 days[1], awaiting the signal that a successful fertilization and implantation has occurred. Without this signal, the remaining cells also die off, the Estrogen drops to its baseline level, and the bleeding starts in anticipation of another try.

In reality, the cycles of women have nothing to do with the cycles of the moon, except for the coincidence that both are around 28 days[2]. And with women born all year long, maturing at different rates and seasons, and

---

[1] This is one of the interesting features of the female menstrual cycle. The variability seen in the menstrual cycle of some women is in the first half, the Follicular Phase. The second half (Luteal Phase) is surprisingly stable at 14 days, +/- 1.5 days. This is also the reason we can guess the date of ovulation in retrospect, but trying to anticipate fertility – the Rhythm Method – is fraught with failure risk.

[2] There's evidence that the moon's orbit around the earth is slowing down. So, did women have cycles less than 28 days in the distant past? How would one go about finding out?

their menstrual cycles interrupted by childbirth and hormonal contraception, no two random women would be expected to have synchronized cycles. And yet if you talk to a group of menstruating women who live in close proximity to each other for an extended period of time (such as Sororities), you will invariably hear stories that they seem to have their periods at about the same time. Truth or urban legend? With the story being repeated by numerous groups of women over the years, it was inevitable that someone would look into it. And as it happens, I attended a lecture by one such inquisitive experimenter.

He began by conducting surveys of groups of freshman girls living in Sororities. Limiting the study to women who were not on any hormonal medication, he noted that their cycles at the beginning of the school term were randomly scattered throughout the month, as expected. Interestingly, by the end of the academic year, many of the girls had synchronized, some by moving their cycles forward, others by lagging behind. It appeared there was some truth to the rumors after all.

The next point of curiosity was, did the women average out their cycles, or was there a single point that they all used for synchronization. And how would this point be determined? Assuming the latter, and suspecting the origin of the point, with the next group of women he also asked personality questions, such as which girl was considered the leader, the decision maker, the natural head of the group – the alpha female, as it were. Collecting menstrual data for this group over the next year, an even more interesting pattern emerged. If the alpha female had regular cycles, in most instances her cycles maintained their rhythm. It was the other girls that altered their cycles to synchronize with the alpha.

It would appear that the fascinating nature of women has no bounds.

So then the question becomes, what is the mechanism, the signal that tells the beta females what the alpha is doing, and when. The experimenter suspected the signal was similar to pheromones, which is olfactory in nature. The odor detecting neuronal cells at the top of the nasal sinus (deep within the nose) lead into one of the more primitive portions of the brain, close to the center that regulates body cycles, including the menstrual cycle in females. Working with this assumption, he had the previously identified alpha females wear special secretion collecting inserts (cotton balls basically) in their underwear and underarms for each day of their cycles. The organic compounds on these balls were then extracted and used to saturate nasal inserts that were in turn given to women on different portion of their cycles. I don't know if the results were ever published, but during the lecture he claimed that he could alter the cycles of individual women by using the timed secretions of alpha females. Questions that I would have liked to have answered include: would the secretions of one alpha female alter the cycles of another alpha, or would it depend on how high on the totem pole each woman was? I would also like to know if women trying to control their irregular cycles would be willing to wear, up their nostrils, cotton swabs containing genital and underarm secretions of a stranger. Is menstrual irregularity ever that big a life event?

* * *

As the woman ages, the existing follicles in her ovaries continue to be consumed every month. And as she gets older, the vigorous, quick responding follicles are used up first, since they are the most sensitive to the signals from the brain. The follicles that are less than prime, the ones that need more of a kick to get them going, are the ones that are recruited as the woman gets older. And at that point during some months the amount of signal necessary exceeds the brain's production capacity. And therefore, no follicle wins the race, resulting in failed ovulation and the cause of the menstrual irregularity many women experience during the approach to menopause. And when the follicle pool is finally exhausted, the ovary's Estrogen production plummets. The brain, seeing this hormone reduction, increases its secretion of stimulating signal in an attempt to get things going, and this is believed to underly the bane of the older woman, the symptoms of menopause.

So, can a woman delay the onset of menopause by suppressing ovulation via long-term use of birth control pills? Unfortunately, not, since the pill suppresses ovulation, but the underlying recruitment is still underway, and the pool of follicles continues to get consumed. There are ways to shut down the process completely, but the side effects are serious, even perilous, to a healthy, prolonged life, and so these medicines are used to treat serious conditions, and even then, for a limited length of time.

* * *

As noted, in a normal 28-day cycle, ovulation occurs around day 13-14, and given the survival of sperm in the female genital tract, fertilization can occur one to two days earlier or later around this point. That is an average, and it not an absolute number. Typical sperm deposit from a healthy male can contain up to 200 million sperm, found within the vagina immediately after intercourse. Vaginal secretions are acidic, and not very hospitable to sperm, so this horde has to fight madly, like live eels on a hot frying pan, and find their way to the cervix, where a much more hospitable environment awaits. About one percent of the initial horde will make it past this first obstacle, and about half of this group will make it into the uterus. Interestingly, sperm initially would have difficulty fertilizing an egg, as the enzyme in the container at the front (used to dissolve the egg membrane and allow penetration) is not very active. After penetrating the cervix, certain compounds present in the secretions and the passage of time activate the enzymes and markedly improve fertilization ability.

From the uterus, the sperm have to travel the length of the fallopian tubes and find their way to the egg, somewhere in the distal end. Statistically another half of the sperm will make the wrong turn and go down the dead-end alley of the non-ovulating side[1]. The number of sperm continues to decrease along the path, until roughly 200 sperm will make it to the vicinity of the egg – about one out of every million that were initially present. Then there ensues a mad dash to penetrate the protective layer of cells left over from the ovary and still attached to the egg (the 'Cumulus Oophorus' – literally, the cloud of the egg), and achieve fertilization. As soon as one sperm gets thru, the figurative door snaps shut on the toes of the rest, and fertilization can take place.

Is it possible for two sperm to simultaneously get thru, and cause double fertilization? Yes, and although very rare, the result is an embryo with 69 chromosomes (instead of 46; 23 from each parent), and three sets of sex chromosomes. These fetuses have a very rare chance, although not unheard, of surviving to birth. They present with a multitude of serious abnormalities[2].

The actual fertilization is the union and mixing of the DNA from the mother with the DNA from the father, resulting in a complete set and a resultant unique individual.

---

[1] It wouldn't surprise me a bit to find out that the egg and/or ovary on the ovulating side put out some kind of signal that guides the sperm down the right path. Nature has a wonderful habit of working that way to make things more efficient.
[2] See Plate-8, A & B.

Why such a waste of production of sperm? At least from one perspective, this is a way of ensuring the success of the fittest. A microscopic examination of sperm within a fresh ejaculate reveals a multitude of abnormal forms (double heads, double tails, bizarre bodies, etc.) as well as dysfunctions (slow swimmers, circular swimmers, uncoordinated tail and body action). The great race to the waiting egg serves to eliminate all but the healthiest, the most robust.

I have often wondered if elimination of this filtering mechanism has negative consequences.

ICSI – Intra-Cytoplasmic Sperm Injection, pronounced 'ECK-see' – is an infertility procedure during which individual sperm, based on visual appearance, are selected from a slide, picked up and manually injected into the egg, which is then implanted in the uterus, in an in-vitro procedure. There are also instances wherein individual sperm (spermatozoa) are collected directly from the testicle in infertile men and used to achieve fertilization.

In the subsequent studies of intellectual and developmental milestones of these individuals, they appear to have progressed normally. But there is much more that makes us human than physical development and intellectual milestones.

Prolapses and Pessaries

Sometimes when I look back, I realize how particularly fortunate I was during my medical education, both in medical school and during residency, having mostly to do with the caliber and unique expertise of some of the physicians I served under. One particular example centered on an elderly Gynecologist, Dr. Richert Taylor[1]. He came across as ancient and long overdue for retirement, but the depth and breadth of his medical knowledge I always found amazing. While some of my fellow residents found his constant recollections and anecdotal stories stodgy, I always made time to listen respectfully. In turn, he confidently shared many of the skills he had picked up over decades of practice, some of which were no longer being extensively taught.

One skill that he shared in detail was the appropriate selection and application of Pessaries.

Humans, with our upright gait, put a significant stress on the pelvic floor. The floor refers to the muscle layer and associated ligaments that support the pelvic organs[2]. When one is standing upright, the bones of the pelvis form a funnel, with a large opening at the top, and the slightly smaller opening at the bottom. What supports everything are strong, multi-layered crisscrossing sheets of muscle lining the bottom opening, pierced by small outlets for the bowel and bladder. To appreciate the load on this layer, one has to consider not only the weight of everything laying on top, but the pressure pulses created from walking, running, coughing, straining during constipation, sit-ups, and any other activity that involves

---

[1] His real name.
[2] In women, the reproductive organs, bladder, rectum, and whatever loops of bowel work their way down.

tightening of the abdominal muscles. The pelvic floor does an admirable job holding things up for a lifetime, and in men rarely causes issues. But in women, there is one more demand that has to be met. Not only is the floor weakened by the opening of the vagina, but during childbirth this opening is stretched and strained even further while accommodating the passage of the fetus, whose head is just about the size of the pelvic outlet. And if this passage causes tears in the muscle fibers or ligaments, there is rarely adequate healing. As a result, women have a disproportionate problem with pelvic floor issues. This is especially true of the ones that have experienced multiple vaginal deliveries, large babies or difficult deliveries.

The problems usually present themselves after menopause. This is a time marked by progressive muscle weakness (from normal age-related atrophy and hormone decrease), increasing weight gain (which puts additional stress on the pelvic floor), and lack of exercise.

The usual first sign is increasing incidence of urine loss with coughing, sneezing and activities involving sudden tightening of the abdominal muscles. Show me a post-menopausal mother jumping on a trampoline, and I can usually show you a pair of stained underwear.

While this may have been a problem for many women when they were younger, it becomes progressive with age and, at some point, may cross the line from nuisance to embarrassment. Another frequently mentioned problem is pain with intercourse[1].

---

[1] Important to recognize that pain with intercourse, especially after menopause, can have a myriad of causes, each of which needs to be investigated and treated.

As the woman ages, the issues with pelvic floor weakness naturally tend to progress. While the musculature weakens, the supporting ligaments of the uterus also weaken. And so, one finds the uterus progressively descending into the vagina. This process can continue until the cervix actually protrudes outside[1], and in extreme cases, the entire vagina turns inside out, protruding outside the body and carrying the uterus with it[2]. And since the bladder is attached to the lower segment of the uterus, the bladder often follows the crowd[3]. But since the urethra (draining the bladder to the outside) is attached to a different layer, it stays in place, which means the urethra now has a kink, making urination difficult or impossible. Unless the woman, or a willing assistant, pushes everything back up inside, allowing the urethra to straighten out and do its job.

A number of surgical repairs are available, from simple office procedures to diminish frequency of leakage, to minimally invasive procedures to repair the prolapse and provide support, to procedures involving complete hysterectomy and restructuring of the entire pelvic support layer. The more involved procedures require that the patient be healthy enough to endure the surgery, and her pelvic tissues robust enough to heal and form satisfactory results.

* * *

Dorothy was a referral from one of our local nursing homes, scheduled within a month after I started my private medical practice. I walked into the examination room to find an elderly lady, stooped by the ravages of

---

[1] For the curious, the medical term is 'Procidentia'.
[2] See plate-18B.
[3] Isolated bladder prolapse can also occur, especially in women who have had a hysterectomy, creating a 'Cystocele'. The rectum can also prolapse, a 'Rectocele'.

age and time. She was thin to the point of being frail, with wispy white hair, and movements that were slow and deliberate in an obvious attempt to minimize arthritic pain. Upon introduction she glanced up with eyes that were surprisingly bright and clear islands of blue, surrounded by an endless ocean of wrinkles. She was pushing 100 years of age, having been born just before the 20th Century, in the centennial of the American Civil war, and had outlived all of her generation, and most of the next. I also quickly discovered that her mind was still sharp, her memories intact, and that I was interacting with a walking, talking, encyclopedic history book. She also still retained the modesty of her generation, but her medical issue was severe enough that she was willing for forgo all decorum in her quest for relief.

Dorothy had been blessed with four children, all healthy, robust vaginal births, and delivered at home[1]. She had dealt with increasing urinary incontinence throughout her adult life, and the problem had become markedly worse after menopause. Her husband had passed away decades earlier, and she had not been sexually active for many years prior, but had noticed a sense of vaginal fullness and pressure. This had become worse over the years, and was inevitably accompanied by the presence of a mass that initially would present at the vaginal opening, as a bulge, during straining. The bulge had become more prominent, and slower to receded, until it became a permanent presence. The facility nurses had seen this issue in many other patients, and did not seem particularly impressed or concerned.

Until Dorothy started having difficulty emptying her bladder, and finally until she could no longer initiate a stream. At this point someone on the staff had to push everything back up and hold it in place to allow

---

[1] She had outlived all but one – an unfair and cruel twist of fate.

urination. Now the patient's nuisance was becoming a staff nuisance, and a real problem, and hence the referral.

An examination quickly confirmed the diagnosis. The walls of the vagina, having been outside of the body for years, had taken on the texture and appearance of thin leather. The atrophied, long disused cervix was visible as a tiny dimple at the end of the bulge, and the small uterus could be readily felt within the mass. The entire collection could easily be pushed back up into the body, and would just as easily slide back out.

Dorothy needed a more practical solution, but her age, her frailty, and the atrophied and distorted collection of her remaining pelvic support could not handle a surgical repair. Her urinary problems could be addressed with a catheter and a urine bag, but left in place permanently, a urinary catheter will inevitably lead to a bladder infection, which at her age could rapidly become a deadly kidney infection.

And that's when Richert's lessons in pessaries and their use came into play. While most Gynecologists are familiar with pessaries, very few of the younger generation know how to evaluate and fit one to a patient.

Pessaries were invented as a solution for prolapse, long before the modern surgical techniques were developed. Even before they were medical devices, women would try and minimize prolapse by inserting a wad of cloth, an apple, or similar object into the vagina to improve the support and prevent prolapse.

Today pessaries are a varied collection of devices, from twisted metal squares, covered in latex, to disks resembling contraceptive diaphragms, to donut shaped balloons that can be inflated and deflated with a squeeze pump and a simple ball valve[1]. Each form comes in a variety of sizes, and all of them are essentially designed to be inserted into the vagina in order to improve the support of the pelvic floor and prevent or minimize prolapse.

In this case, given Dorothy's extensive atrophy and severity of prolapse, I felt that the balloon pessary was most appropriate, and thanks to my earlier training, I knew how to determine the appropriate size. I explained my recommendation to the patient, and she jumped at the opportunity for relief from her daily struggle and embarrassment.

Dorothy returned a week or so later, once I had ordered and received the device. Also present was one of the nursing staff from the facility. I demonstrated the device, provided instructions on its use, and inserted it in place along with some ointment to allow her body to better handle the intrusion. The balloon was inflated, the device stayed in place, and she was dismissed with a follow-up visit in one week to see how she was doing, how it was tolerated, and if the device was working as expected, or popped out into the toilet bowl each time she strained to void.

I walked into the room at the follow-up visit totally unprepared for the reception. As soon as she saw me, Dorothy rose from the exam table faster than I would have expected, rushed over and gave me an extended hug, and with tears in her bright eyes profusely thanked me for altering her life and allowing her to look forward to another day of living. Her accolades continued to the point that I became embarrassed and changed the subject.

---

[1] See Plate-18A for representative examples.

It would appear that the device was working as promised. One would never expect a simple rubber balloon to have such a profound impact on the life of someone Dorothy's age.

I did not hear from Dorothy or the nursing staff again, and out of curiosity I had my staff call and inquire. We learned that sadly, Dorothy had passed away less than a month after her pessary fitting. She didn't live to be 100, and all of her memories and recollections of history, and her participation in it, were buried with her. I reconciled myself with the thought that in one small way I made the last days of her life a bit more comfortable.

* * *

As a final note, the nursing home staff removed and cleaned the pessary after Dorothy's death, and returned it to our office in a brown paper bag, in case we had someone else in need. The reuse of the device would have been inappropriate, but my office staff decided to create a plaque, crowning me as the 'Pessary King' and mounting Dorothy's pessary on it. It was a bit silly, and nothing that I would display in public, but knowing the story of the centenarian behind the little latex balloon led me to hold on to it for years afterwards.

Obstetrics

The practice of obstetrics, the care of the pregnant woman and her delivery, as a branch of medicine, only goes back about 100 or so years. Prior, all the way back to the beginning of recorded history, pregnant women were tended to by other women, usually family members, and hopefully an experienced attendant at delivery. Midwifery per se was not established until late 18th century, and not recognized as a profession until the 19th century. This was also the time when some medical men began to express an interest in attending the delivery process, a practice which was initially frowned upon by most of their colleagues, and even labeled as a form of perversion.

With continued scientific advances and improved knowledge of anatomy and the physiologic processes involved in pregnancy and delivery, the practice of Obstetrics gained traction in the medical mainstream. But it was not without its own tragedy. From mid-1800's to the beginning of the 20th century, men of medicine promoted delivery at hospitals, attended to by professional physicians known as Obstetricians. But delivery during this time was fraught with danger for the mother, in the form of a post-delivery fever known as Puerperal Fever, or Childbirth Fever. It was an invariably fatal infection, usual onset within two to three days of delivery, with no known cause or treatment. What was interesting, and should have served as a warning, was the fact that the disease was common in deliveries attended to by male physicians, but very rare in at-home deliveries attended to by midwives. One would think the link would be obvious to any person of intelligence looking at the numbers. But even after a physician[1], in the mid-1800's, demonstrated that the rate of infection could be markedly reduced to less than one percent by the simple act of hand washing before the delivery, there was resistance to

---

[1] Ignaz Philipp Semmelweis.

accept the practice. It wasn't until the proposition and acceptance of germ theory in the early 1900's that hand washing before attending birth came to be accepted. But in the intervening 50 years an untold number of mothers suffered and died unnecessarily.

And then there were Cesarean deliveries.

Historically, description of the delivery of a baby from the mother's abdomen goes back to the ancient history. There are references in Greek, Egyptian, Roman, and other ancient cultures of babies delivered via an abdominal incision. And of course, there's the story of Julius Caesar being delivered abdominally, supposedly the origin of the name. History records Caesar's mother as having lived to give vaginal birth to a number of other children, an even more unlikely possibility[1]. All of these stories must be approached with caution, for they likely represent folklore rather than fact. Given the complications associated with an abdominal delivery, from ignorance about the anatomy, to the massive blood loss given the failure to close the uterine incision, to the high risk of infection, it is unlikely that any mother would have survived. It would be unlikely but possible that some babies, delivered from mothers that were dead, dying, or mortally gored, may have lived. There were undoubtedly isolated cases where a mother and baby both survived following the procedure, but Caesarean delivery became a viable alternative to vaginal delivery only in the mid-1800's. That was the time when closing of the uterine incision came into practice. This simple step helped to staunch the bleeding and limit the spread of infection, the two-headed monster that freely consumed lives earlier.

---

[1] Julius Caesar did proclaim during his reign that with any dead or dying mother the baby should be delivered abdominally, probably as a nod to religious or social requirements; a more likely origin for the name of the procedure.

71

The Beauty of It All

The course of a normal pregnancy, from the moment of conception to delivery at term, encompasses, on average, 38 weeks or 280 days[1]. Since most women cannot nail down the date of conception, but do recall the date of their last menses (with conception following, on average, two weeks later), we use 40 weeks as the length of the average pregnancy. This of course is giving credit to the mother for two weeks when she actually wasn't pregnant, but no one seems to mind. The developmental changes that lead from a single fertilized cell at the moment of conception to a fully formed human being are more complicated than anything you can point to in the known universe. We crudely understand the steps and the results, but what intricate, intertwined steps result in one clump of cells becoming bone and an adjacent clump becoming nerves, while another neighbor becomes muscle, is well beyond our grasp. While thru dogged research we have a good understanding of the changes involved, no one has glimpsed the blueprint, understood the coding, the directions, nor the underlying rules and orders.

After fertilization, the implant within the pregnant uterus has three structures. First is the developing and growing fetus, second is the placenta, and third is the amniotic sac. All three arise from the fertilized egg, and bear the DNA of the fetus[2]. The amniotic fluid represents the excretions of the fetus, primarily in the form of urine. During the first half

---

[1] Conception occurs not in the uterus, as commonly believed, but around the area of the ovary, or in the first part of the fallopian tube. The egg, now an ovum, then hangs loose for up to three days before moving into the uterus and starting to dig and implanting. Should it arrive any sooner, the necessary tools for implantation are absent, and the ovum will be lost with the next menstrual flow.

[2] Why the mother's immune system doesn't attack the foreign tissues of the fetus during development is one of the ongoing mysteries of pregnancy.

of the pregnancy, before the fetal skin becomes impermeable, a fair amount of the amniotic fluid is seepage thru the skin. There's also a small contribution from the lungs, during respiration activity. And yes, the fetus does breathe, going thru the motions, although all of its oxygen needs are met via the placenta. A critical part of the development of the lungs depends on the fetus 'breathing' with amniotic fluid moving into and then out of the lungs. In some cases, this process is hindered, or completely blocked. Some examples are cases when the trachea – the tube leading from the back of the throat into the lungs – fails to normally develop, or if the diaphragm – the muscular separation between the chest and the abdomen – has a defect and intestines intrude into the chest. These unfortunate fetuses fail to properly develop the lungs, and in the absence of early intervention, are destined to die at birth when the link to the mother is broken.

The placenta is an organ found only in mammals, and thought to be a significant contribution to the success of the order on the planet. It is one of the first tissues to develop after implantation, as it must, in order to nourish the pregnancy. It is truly an organ, as complex and necessary as the kidneys or the liver in the adult. It has a multifaceted role, for it is also a gland, producing a number of substances and hormonal signals to benefit the growing fetus. One of these lets the mother know she's pregnant, preventing the initiation of the next period, which would cause loss of the pregnancy[1]. Another signal initiates the rapid growth and enlargement of the mother's blood supply to the uterus. Yet another makes the mother a semi-diabetic, raising her blood sugar to provide energy for the baby. The suppression of the mother's immune system is modulated by factors also produced by the placenta. This organ also has a

---

[1]This hormone, human Chorionic Gonadotropin, or hCG, is the basis of all pregnancy tests.

number of active means of transporting nutrients to the fetus – think of a pump, as active in this case means the level on the fetal side are actually higher than the level on the mother's side. The placenta continues to grow alongside the fetus, enabling life, only to be separated from the newborn baby, and disrespectfully discarded after birth. Some societies encourage the mother to consume the placenta after delivery, for it is a rich source of protein and nutrients. If one is so inclined, a search on the internet will reveal similar rituals in developed countries, usually accompanied by recipes for such delicacies as 'placenta lasagna' and 'placenta stew'. I have had a number of patients that requested to take their placenta home after delivery, and I know one of them would dig a hole in her back yard, place the placenta in the bottom, and plant a tree on top. She had four children, and I suspect four very nicely fertilized trees growing on her property. One patient, who always came to the office with her service dog, requested that the placenta be fed to the animal at delivery. The line was drawn on that one, knowing for a fact that the hospital would never allow a dog, service or otherwise, in the delivery room, much less the ward. One also can't help but disdain the thought of the animal engorging on the placenta, and then hungrily eyeing the newborn, who was after all, made up of the same tissue flavor.

* * *

Any text on Obstetrics will have pictures of the developing fetus. What they all lack is a demonstration of the complexity of the organism, for no 2-dimensional drawing or photo could ever reveal that level. Of necessity, they also show the fetus at incorrect sizes during development. Only by studying a text on embryology can one begin to get an idea of what is going on during those incredible nine months.

It is interesting to note that some Embryologists[1] will actually compare the progressive stages of the developing fetus to what they interpret as the course of evolution on the planet[2]. The initial stage, the zygote, resembles single cell organisms, such as amoeba; the next stage resembles primitive sponges; the one after hollow animals such as jellyfish, and so on up the evolutionary ladder. There may be a point to this, since the human embryo at four weeks gestation is indistinguishable from a chicken embryo, and you can't tell the human embryo from the chimpanzee until after ten weeks of gestation. During early development human embryos demonstrate gills and a tail, and webbed hands and feet, all of which disappear by birth – although sometimes the programmed loss does not occur, giving rise to trash journalism fodder.

Some systems, out of necessity, begin functioning much sooner than others. The heart is visibly beating on ultrasound at six weeks (four weeks post conception; it actually is active around day 16 of life), and the thyroid gland is the first out of the gate, producing hormone at around ten weeks. Obstetrical texts will tell you that all of the definitive organs are represented in some form by eight weeks, and in their definitive form and location by 12 weeks[3]. The wonder is in the fact that the eight-week embryo is about the size of a kidney bean, and at 12 weeks about three-inches long[4]. From 12 weeks on, the only significant change is the growth of the fetus, and maturation of the various systems. There are endless forms of modeling going on of course. As one example, the finger bones

---

[1] Specialist in the development of a fetus.
[2] While I realize that there are a lot of educated people that do not believe in evolution, preferring a literal translation of Biblical creation, I've always found the argument puzzling, for I see no incompatibility with evolution theory and the existence of a creator.
[3] Except the testes, which do not descend into the scrotum until the third trimester.
[4] See Plate-3.

resemble full hands, but the fingers are fused until 20 weeks, with the toes separating somewhat later. The eyelids finally open around the beginning of the third trimester, and the fetus begins blinking. The ears begin functioning at 18-20 weeks, and the fetus begins responding to noise by 24 weeks. It's interesting to note that the hearing of the fetus (indeed of babies) is exquisitely sensitive, which by definition means fragile. I would hesitate to encourage a pregnant woman, after 20 weeks, to attend rock concerts, shooting ranges, drag races, or other venues notable for loud, sharp and repetitive noise.

The digestive system is quiescent until the third trimester, at which point the swallowing of the amniotic fluid begins to form meconium – fetal stool, and the bane of obstetricians, midwives, and pediatricians. The circulatory system of the fetus is also unusual, with three bypasses that are absent in normal adults. These help direct blood from the placenta, via the umbilical cord, into the general circulation of the fetus, bypassing the lungs which are non-functioning, and bypassing the liver, which is not involved in digestion. At birth, with the first breath, the lungs inflate, which shuts one bypass, the loss of the placental flow shuts off the second, and the resulting pressure alterations and flow changes shuts off the third. And we have an autonomous being, able to breathe and digest on its own. And cry, to let everyone know it can do the former and needs the latter.

* * *

Up until the time of birth, the fetus is sterile. It has not been exposed to any bacteria or viruses, and its immune system lacks the ability to mount a defensive response. The immune system begins maturing around 24 weeks, and is in place by the term birth. Sometime shortly before birth, based on some vague signal, the mother passes a load of antibodies to the fetus to protect it against infection in the immediate post-birth period[1,2].

At birth the baby's immune system is still not completely mature, although it is fully self-aware. That is, if any tissue from another being is transplanted, the baby's body will immediately mount an aggressive rejection response. This self-awareness seems to develop around the 20th week of gestation. Before this point, the immune system is naïve, and will accept any foreign tissue and label it, forever, as its own. If at some point in the future all pregnancies were to be inoculated with some common human HLA antigen[3] – that is, a common marker identifying all humans as self – we would share this commonality with everyone else that was so inoculated. Transplants would then become routine and free of the need for rejection suppression. Getting a kidney from a stranger would be no more complicated than if your own kidney was moved from one side to the other. I've met many physicians who view this as a noble, Utopian goal. Others see it as opening a Pandora's box, for what is to prevent couples from having babies just to provide some vital organ or tissue to an existing ailing child, or humans of lower social status to be viewed as organ warehouses for the well-to-do[4].

---

[1] Antibodies are proteins that attack foreign intruders. They are produced in response to past infections, so the mother is in effect protecting her fetus against known infections in her environment.

[2] Occasionally infections in utero can and do occur, usually with devastating results, since the fetus doesn't have an immune system, and depends on the mother to clear out infections, and the mother's immune system is hindered in mounting its defenses within the fetus, a privileged and off-limit area.

[3] Human Lymphocyte Antigen. This is the primary marker that labels each person for the immune system.

[4] Already occurring, and documented, in China and India.

Julie and the Turtle

Somewhere in the past our ancestors gave up four-legged gait for walking upright. During that transition the legs became more parallel to the body axis and the pelvis tilted to better carry the weight. The resultant changes made the birth canal narrower and more angled. At the same time, the continued advancement of the brain resulted in babies with larger heads. As a result of this combination, humans, of all mammals, suffer one of the greatest difficulties in giving birth. During the age of industrialization, better nutrition and reduction of diseases and parasites resulted in a continual increase in the size of the term fetus. Data from the early 20th century shows average birth weight to be right under seven pounds, while the average birth weight in the United States today is pushing eight pounds. In the meantime, the accommodating female pelvis has hardly grown in size over the last 50 years. And insurance companies wonder why the cesarean rate is so high (less than 10% in the 1950's, up to 40% or more today). And when the mother does successfully push the baby's head out, there can arise one of the worst complications of delivery that obstetricians have had to deal with in their careers.

* * *

Shoulder Dystocia is a medical term describing a condition wherein the head of the baby has successfully delivered, but the shoulders are trapped. Given the force of contractions during labor, pushing the baby into the birth canal, combined with the ability of the fetal head to change shape[1], almost any reasonably sized baby's head can be delivered, even thru a

---

[1] The bones of the baby's skull are not fused at the time of birth, allowing the head to change shape and better accommodate the passage thru the birth canal.

narrow birth canal[1]. But often in the case of large babies, the rest of the body, especially the shoulders, can become entrapped. The normal position of the baby at the moment of birth is with the shoulders up and down within the birth canal, and the back of the baby to the left or right of the mother. With broad shoulders, large babies, or a mother with a marginally narrow pelvis, what can happen is successful delivery of the head, followed by what is colloquially called the 'turtle sign', or retraction of the baby's head back against the opening of the birth canal. This is often the first and only indication that the anterior shoulder is trapped behind the mother's pubic bone, with the posterior shoulder jammed against the inside of her pelvis. The medical texts advise immediately declaring an emergency, and a number of maneuvers and steps to be taken in order to facilitate delivery. For at this point, the baby's body is squeezing the umbilical cord and cutting off respiration, and the natural pressure to deliver is stretching the nerve fibers leading from the baby's neck down to the arm. Some of the recommended steps involve introducing the hand into the birth canal and attempting to rotate the shoulder from behind the pubic bone. What the books do not reveal is that with the baby jammed up against the mother there is nary any room to slip one's hand and try to rotate the jammed shoulder, or introduce a pair of scissors to cut the mother's tissue from the posterior opening of the vagina all the way back into the rectum to create more space. The final maneuvers, twisting the baby back into and up the birth canal followed by an emergency cesarean, or introducing an instrument to intentionally fracture the baby's clavicle[2] (allowing the jammed shoulder to move

---

[1] My personal record for vaginal delivery is 12lb-3oz. The record for vaginal delivery at my training institution was 13+ pounds. The worldwide confirmed record for a baby that was born alive is 22 pounds. One can only cringe at the thought of what that mother must have endured. See Plate-12A for a representative example.
[2] Clavicle: collar bone.

tighter against the baby's chest) I have never had to attempt, nor have I had the opportunity to observe.

Not that long ago, one of the maneuvers recommended, and routinely performed, was the splitting apart of the mother's pubic bone. The front of the pubic bone is a fusion of two halves of the pelvis held together by a dense cartilage. If the cartilage can be cut in a timely manner, the two halves of the pelvis separate and ample room is created to deliver the baby. This was initially done with a pair of heavy scissors (shears), as using a scalpel carries the risk of cutting into the bladder, which is immediately behind the pubic bone. Unfortunately, the process is slow and excruciatingly painful. In an attempt to expedite the process, someone invented a roller chain with teeth on the outside, moving around two sprockets, and driven with a crank. Thus, was created the origin of the first chainsaw.

How far we have come.

At best, there is a traumatic delivery of a limp but otherwise normal baby. At worst, there can be permanent nerve damage, rendering useless the baby's arm, or the baby can suffer, within a matter of 5-10 minutes, permanent, irreversible brain damage. There are folklores in every major hospital of a baby's head being separated from the rest of the body during vigorous attempts at delivery, but these thoughts are best not dwelt upon, and hopefully they have no basis in fact.

I had observed a number of instances of shoulder dystocia during my training, all of which were successfully handled without any long-term consequences. After starting private practice, the turtle would rear its ugly head periodically, but was always kept at bay with appropriate efforts and timely interventions.

And then along came Julie.

Julie was a pleasant 22-year-old approaching the end of her first pregnancy. Her weight gain thru the course of the pregnancy had been normal, she was of normal height and weight, and while in my opinion her pelvis was somewhat narrow front to back, it did not rule out a trial of labor[1]. Given that her baby's estimated weight at 39 weeks, when labor ensued, was around eight pounds, I allowed things to progress. And progress they did, until the head popped out, and immediately pulled back into a severe 'turtle sign'. First things first, and the first thing I did was take a deep breath, count to ten (truthfully, it was probably more like three), and in a calm voice designed not to overly frighten the mother, notified the attending nurse to ring the emergency call light and notify the pediatrician on call[2]. The mother was instructed to bring her knees up close to her chest, the nurse instructed to push above the pubic bone to attempt to dislodge the jammed shoulder from above, and I attempted to introduce my hand into the already tightly filled birth canal to carry out the requisite maneuvers.

I don't remember how long it took, and I don't remember how many times and how many different maneuvers I tried. I do know that I managed to deliver an 8-pound, 6-ounce, slightly blue and very limp baby

---

[1] After performing 10,000+ pelvic exams, one becomes rather adept at measuring the inlet and outlet of the birth canal with a simple although somewhat uncomfortable exam in the office. The fine nuances of pelvic measurements – pelvimetry – require an x-ray or CT scan, which are rarely indicated. I can comfortably measure the front-back diameter of the pelvis with my manual exam to an accuracy of +/- 1 cm, or 1/3 of an inch.

[2] Obstetricians and pilots are, in my opinion, the two professions who learn early in their careers to deal with emergencies in a calm manner, with a deep, slow and reassuring voice. The deepening timber of the voice, and the reduction in the speed of annunciation are good indications of the severity of the emergency in both instances.

boy who spent a couple of days in the intensive care nursery recovering from the traumatic birth. He had no broken bones, no nerve injuries, no brain damage, and grew into a precocious and troublesome young man. It remained the subject of one of my recurring nightmares, and the worst case of shoulder dystocia ever in my career.

And to no one's surprise, about two years later, Julie showed up pregnant again. She had vague memories of what she had endured, and yet pleaded with me to find a way to avoid a cesarean. So, at 37.5 weeks, with her cervix already demonstrating pre-labor changes, the baby's estimated weight by ultrasound right at seven pounds, and her pelvis already having been prepared by the previous delivery, I successfully induced her.

In short order she delivered vaginally a baby whose weight was dead-on the pre-delivery estimate, and a full pound and a half less than his brother's. And I managed to experience the second worst case of shoulder dystocia ever in my career.

It's enough to make one look forward to retirement.

Serena, The Guardian Angel

You would think in this day and age a spontaneous vaginal delivery for a second time mom would be an uncomplicated affair. I certainly thought so after attending one delivery around midnight, following about six hours of labor. The baby, average in weight, had delivered without the need for an episiotomy[1]. Mom had done well afterwards, and had successfully nursed her newborn by the time I finished the paperwork and left for an attempt at getting some sleep before office the next day. Shortly after arriving home, I received a call from the floor nurse – never a good sign in the middle of the night. Seems she was concerned about swelling and discoloration of the genital area of the recently delivered patient. Not to worry, as sometimes blood vessels rupture during delivery, and some bruising results. I recommended application of ice and pressure and confidently predicted resolution by morning. About the time I dozed off, dreaming that I may yet get some sleep, another call comes in. This time the nurse's voice and tone indicated serious concern, and she reports that despite the previous measures the swelling has markedly increased, and the patient complains of unremitting pain, and an inability to urinate. Looks like it's another trip back to the hospital.

The female reproductive organs, both internal (uterus, cervix, tubes, ovaries, upper part of vagina) and external (lower part of vagina, labia), are supported by a dense network of blood vessels, with many cross connections and numerous origins off of the main vessel leading out of the heart. The average adult female carries around five liters, or five

---

[1] The surgical cut that is made below the vaginal opening, in the area called the perineum. Its purpose is to create a larger opening for the delivery, and to limit tears. Some attendants cut one routinely, others forgo the procedure altogether. I always tried and avoid making the cut unless I felt a tear was imminent.

quarts[1], of blood in their body. This volume increase to about seven and a half liters by the end of pregnancy, and is one reason a woman can lose an impressive amount of blood at delivery and still go home the next day without needing a transfusion. For reference, the average young woman's heart pumps about four liters per minute, increasing to about six liters per minute in a woman by the end of her pregnancy. Therefore, every minute, she is completely circulating about 80% of her blood volume. One can appreciate why a large blood vessel tear can quickly lead to exsanguination – complete loss of blood – and death.

There is no area in the female reproductive region that is fed by a single artery[2], and extensive blockage of blood vessels results in minimal tissue effect. During pregnancy, these cross channels markedly increase in size and number. As an example, in a case of heavy bleeding from the uterus after delivery (usually due to retained fragments of placenta), the surgeon can tie off the main arteries that feed the uterus (and extend up to the ovaries), and both organs will be fine and able to support future ovulation, conception and fetal growth all the way to term. On the down side, any rupture of blood vessels in this region can result in massive blood loss, difficult to control. The other confounding factor is that there is frequent variation in the origin and course of the major blood vessels supplying the female pelvis.

These facts came front and foremost when I examined the patient upon arrival. Her labia were massively swollen, discolored, and a recent blood test hinted that she had lost an additional liter of blood after her delivery

---

[1] A liter is about 6% more than a quart; close enough for this discussion. And four quarts make for a gallon.
[2] Unlike some other organs, such as the eye. The retina of the eye is fed by a single artery, and any blockage in this vessel or its subsequent branches results in irreversible blindness in the areas that are served.

– blood that was collecting under the skin of her external genitals. At this point a catheter was inserted to allow her to empty her bladder[1], and under anesthesia I made an incision in the skin of the offending side and began searching for the source. Unless one has dealt with this situation firsthand, there is no easy way to describe the frustration and desperation at this point. The patient is obviously hemorrhaging, the offending area is open, but the tissues have the consistency of saturated sponge cake – fragile, easily torn, impossible to clamp or suture without causing more tearing and bleeding, and oozing blood everywhere with no visible single source that can be identified and closed. And while earlier the bleeding was somewhat contained by the pressure of the skin, that area was now open and the blood was freely running out. The deeper I probed the more tissue I destroyed, the more frustrating the situation became, and I was obviously contributing to the problem and not the solution. I do not give into panic, and I have never lost a patient, nor been directly involved in the care of a patient that did not survive. But I was suddenly looking at that very possibility, with the added tragedy being it threatened the life of a healthy young woman just recently experiencing uncomplicated childbirth.

I had always been told that I had a guardian angel. Impudently, I had even given her a name, Serena. And at times when I was truly struggling, I would mumble a mantra for help from Serena. But on this night, I became a believer. Our medical institution had just a few months earlier hired a new Interventional Radiologist[2], and this individual came with training and the skills to perform catheter embolization. In this procedure, the Radiologist, while observing a live x-ray screen, runs a long, thin tube into the main artery feeding the area of bleeding, injects a

---

[1] See Plate-4.
[2] A common skill nowadays, but unheard of in a small town during this era.

dye visible under x-ray, and deduces the exact source of the blood loss by following the path of the dye. The catheter is then advanced into the offending area and the bleeding is controlled by injecting beads and compounds that cause immediate clot formation. The offending vessel is therefore closed off, and the surrounding tissues continue to receive oxygen and nutrients via the surrounding circulation.

Fortuitously, the individual trained and skilled in performing this procedure, was at that moment administering anesthesia to the very patient I was struggling to save. When the suggestion was made to attempt the embolization procedure I jumped at the opportunity. The patient was wheeled into the Radiology suite, the procedure was carried out, and in less than half the time that I had spent struggling, the offending blood vessel was identified and clotted off. Turned out this was an unusual connection to the external genitals from a blood vessel originating from the deep pelvis, a vessel I could have never identified from my approach. The blood vessel had been stretched and torn during the delivery, resulting in all of the subsequent problems.

The reduction in active bleeding at this point was a phenomenon to behold. I addressed the smaller oozing vessels and closed the skin over the mess I had made. The patient received multiple units of blood, and went home no wiser as to how close her baby had come to being an orphan on its birth day. God bless that guardian Angel, and God truly bless and keep safe that wonderful Radiologist, who had the training, the necessary skills, the tools and the timing to prevent a tragedy.

As to office the next day, well it just goes to show that when you're young, sleep is overrated.

The Miracle of it All

The bane of the mature woman is her menstrual cycle. Thru out recorded history it has been unfairly associated with physical disability, mental instability, and a vague sense of uncleanliness[1]. Even today related topics such as male impotence are openly discussed and advertised on media, complete with graphic demonstrations. But ads for containment of menstrual blood are obtuse and filled with metaphors. There is also minimal research into menstrual abnormalities, even though by some measures one in four women experience irregular periods, and one in 10 suffer from endometriosis.

* * *

Endometriosis is a term often tossed about in social conversations as an explanation for menstrual pain and cramps above and beyond what would be considered normal. It is however, a well-defined medical condition with significant consequences. It has already been explained that the lining of the uterus is a special layer of tissue, destined for rapid growth over a couple of weeks, followed by degradation and discard over a few days, or sustenance for the developing fetus over 9 months. It can be identified microscopically in the lining of the uterus even in the newborn female baby. And in a minority, although not rarity, of women, it is found focally outside of the uterus, often present as small islands within the pelvis. These islands respond to the normal hormonal signals of the cycles, growing and subsequently bleeding and breaking down. But they grow where they do not belong, and the subsequent bleeding has nowhere to

---

[1] A number of primitive cultures banish women to outlying areas during their menses, as it is felt they are unclean during this time and cannot be in the same unit as a family's religious icons.

go. Based upon the location of the implants, a variety of symptoms can present during each menstrual cycle. These can range from mild to severe abdominal cramps, to urinary symptoms, to changes and pain with bowel movements.

The reason for development of endometriosis remains a mystery. The most frequent listed reason is reverse flow of menstrual blood thru the fallopian tube and into the abdominal cavity, where some of the still living lining cells can implant and grow.

If only it were that simple.

There have been reported cases of endometriosis being identified outside of the abdomen. In my training I was peripherally involved in the case of a woman who experienced a repetitive, painful pneumothorax[1], which seemed to coincide with her menstrual cycle. Eventually, out of frustration, someone biopsied the affected area of the lung and the subsequent report from the pathologist describing endometrial tissue as the source of the air leak surprised all involved. There have even been reported cases of endometriosis within the brain[2].

Given the persistent and usually progressive symptoms, and the consequences, which can include infertility, the condition has a number of therapies, from hormonal treatment to surgical excision or laser destruction of the individual lesions.

---

[1] Pneumothorax: air present in the chest outside of the lung sacs.
[2] Before anyone rushes to explain their headache during the menstrual cycle as a case of cerebral endometriosis, I should point out that the condition is incredibly rare, with only a handful of cases reported, and it is usually identifiable on brain imaging.

Extensive endometriosis in the pelvis can lead to scarring (as free blood is a tissue irritant), adhesions (preventing the tube from moving about and picking up the egg), and infertility problems, and demands intervention. One of the dilemmas facing the gynecologist is what to do about scattered small lesions, for destroying or cutting out the lesions during surgery can itself lead to scarring and adhesions, and hormonal treatments have limits on the duration of their use. There are also schools of thought that small endometriosis lesions are quite common, and irrelevant, and symptoms of menstrual cramps or infertility problems are coincidental.

The final answer remains to be seen.

* * *

It is interesting to note that menstrual bleeding is not universal among mammals. Humans only share this trait with chimpanzees, bats, and shrews. All other mammals reabsorb the endometrial lining, rather than shed it. Humans are also the only mammal whose female fertile window is covert[1].

* * *

The typical cycle runs 28 days in most women, and is surprisingly consistent in most of them, so much so that when there is an alteration it invariably leads to an office call or visit. The fertile window during the cycle is typically no more than one to two days. The woman's fertility window opens at ovulation, which is on average about midway between her menses, and closes shortly thereafter. The male contribution extends

---

[1] Perhaps this is the explanation for our sexual overdrive – another unique human trait.

91

that up to 24 hours around ovulation – which is how long sperm will survive in the female genital tract.

The actual fertilization occurs in the opening or along the extension of the fallopian tube, not in the uterus as commonly believed. The fertilized egg – now a zygote – works its way into the uterus, and hopefully by the third day implants and signals the presence of the pregnancy. The fertilized egg can be thought of as 'sticky' after fertilization; if its passage to the uterus is delayed for any reason, it will stick and begin to dig and grow wherever it finds itself. This is medically referred to as an Ectopic Pregnancy; a pregnancy that's located anywhere outside of the normal environment of the uterus.

The most common location of an ectopic pregnancy is within the fallopian tube itself[1]. Due to previous injury or scarring or some failure in the transport of the bundle, the fertilized egg attaches to the lining of the tube, and begins to grow. It performs all of the housekeeping chores that need to be done, including growing a placenta, secreting pregnancy hormones, and developing an embryo. The formation of the early placenta and the associated hormonal secretions cause the nearby blood vessels to enlarge and begin feeding the growing embryo. Unfortunately, the fallopian tube wall is thin and not able to stretch and accommodate a pregnancy much beyond six to eight weeks. The stretching of the tube also causes significant symptoms for the woman, usually represented by one-sided severe cramps and pain. This condition represents a true medical emergency; by the time the symptoms become severe enough to cause the patient to seek help the pregnancy has established a significant blood supply, and is in danger of rupture and massive bleeding into the

---

[1] See Plate-9B.

abdomen. This condition is actually one of the leading causes of death in the early pregnant woman.

Medically there is no alternative but removal of the pregnancy. If the ectopic pregnancy is in its early stages and the tube hasn't ruptured it can be removed without destroying the tube, and without needing a large abdominal incision[1]. There is unfortunately no option for transferring the pregnancy into the uterus for continued growth.

* * *

While I have never personally seen an example, the worst location for an ectopic tubal pregnancy is in the section of the tube after it enters the uterus. This short segment is still not able to accommodate a pregnancy, but being surrounded by uterine muscle, it is able to stretch more and allow the pregnancy to proceed further along. Which in turn means larger blood vessels and more massive bleeding when rupture does occur. Furthermore, being in the top corner of the uterus, there is a real risk that its true nature may be missed during an ultrasound evaluation, leading to false reassurance and further progression along the road to disaster.

While the fallopian tube is the most common site for an ectopic pregnancy, there have been many other sites reported. Ovarian ectopic pregnancy represents a case of the egg being fertilized without ever having left the ovary. This is associated with severe pain and usually, early intervention. There are also numerous reported examples of the early

---

[1] My practicing institution was a Catholic hospital, with a strong advocacy against anything even hinting at abortion. The first time I performed an ectopic removal I was brought before the ethics committee. They wanted a clarification that in the future I could remove the tube with the enclosed pregnancy (a diseased organ), but could not remove just the pregnancy and preserve the tube – an abortion so to speak. The logic behind the mandate defied explanation.

pregnancy implanting within the abdominal cavity, usually attached to the lining, but occasionally on the bowel itself.

An interesting case is attachment to the omentum.

The omentum is a thick lining of fat cells, resembling a curtain, that lies in front of and within loops of bowel. It has a generous blood supply from multiple sources, is freely mobile, and serves as a cushion for the bowel, and secondarily helps to contain any infection within the abdominal cavity. If the fertilized egg should implant onto a portion of the omentum that is away from any attachment, it will find itself in an area that allows growth and advanced development. The abdominal cavity can stretch and accommodate the advancing pregnancy, and the blood supply is adequate for the needs of the fetus all the way to term.

In the meantime, the muscle and lining of the uterus thicken in response to the hormones of the advancing abdominal pregnancy, but the uterus remains a fraction of the size it would normally reach. The mother may notice that her baby is particularly well defined in the abdomen, that the movements are much more noticeable compared to her previous pregnancy, but these are all positive signs and hardly warrant suspicion. A modern ultrasound machine in the hands of a competent ultrasonographer[1] should make the diagnosis obvious, especially early in the pregnancy, but it is possible to miss, particularly if the mother is obese, and most of these cases were reported before the advent of regular use of the technology.

And so the pregnancy proceeds until the day the mother goes into labor, and that's when things really get interesting.

---

[1] A person trained to perform ultrasound examinations of the body.

She starts to feel regular contractions of increasing frequency and intensity, but her cervix refuses to dilate, and the baby hums along nicely without any evidence of the usual signs of stress associated with labor, and without descending into the pelvis. This nonsense goes on for hours or days, until either the mother, the nurses taking care of her, or the physician decide enough is enough, throw in the towel, and proceed with a cesarean delivery. But what is this? As soon as the abdomen is opened, there is the baby in a transparent sac, squinting at the sudden bright light and intrusion, with nary a uterus in the way.

By now the diagnosis is obvious and the baby is delivered, expressing the usual displeasure at the interruption of its daily routine. But the delivery of the placenta – the afterbirth – becomes problematic.

In its natural environment in the uterus, the placenta is deeply implanted, but the actual point of attachment is a layer that easily peels off (imagine Velcro). The attachment is strong enough to allow movement of the baby, and normal flexion of the wall of the uterus from the activities of the mother, but temporary enough to easily and completely separate after birth. And the site of separation is surrounded by dense muscle, able to squeeze off the amble blood supply. Sometimes however, things do go wrong. If the mother has had multiple deliveries, or cesarian deliveries beforehand, the scarring that can occur can prevent the separation of the placenta, which can leave bits of dead tissue behind (with serious risk of infection) or prevent the blood vessels from shutting off (with serious blood loss for the mother). On the other side of the spectrum, the separation can occur prematurely, resulting in bleeding. The blood tends to collect and sometimes forces progressive separation to continue. It also decreases the amount of placenta tending to the baby's needs, and the natural irritation of pooled blood can force the uterus into contracting prematurely, which can only make matters worse.

In the case of an ectopic pregnancy, the placenta is not going to peel off nicely as it does in the uterus, and even if it did, there are no uterine muscles around to squeeze the blood vessels and shut off the massive bleeding[1]. In one reported case, the majority of the placenta was left in place and allowed to absorb over time. This would be fraught with danger, primarily from the risk of an infection getting established in a couple of pounds of dead and dying tissue within the abdomen. In another reported cases the placenta and omentum were dissected out as one unit, and the engorged blood vessels individually tied off – a long, arduous process accompanied by significant blood loss.

* * *

Shelley was a 27-year-old patient of one of our local family practitioners, at 22-weeks' gestation. She had been experiencing worsening abdominal pain, and by the time she presented to the emergency room she was writhing in pain. I was on call and my presence was requested, around 8PM on a weekday. This was Shelley's second pregnancy, and it later came to light that her first pregnancy ended in a miscarriage in early second trimester, and since at the time she was bleeding significantly, the miscarriage was managed with what turned out to have been a difficult D&C[2].

---

[1] At term, one fourth of the mother's heart output, or about 1.5 liters (or 1-3/4 quarts), *per minute,* goes into the circulation for the placenta. Her total blood volume at term is about 7 liters, or 7.5 quarts.
[2] D&C: dilatation and curettage. See definitions.

Leading up to the emergency room visit, Shelley had been experiencing worsening abdominal pain unrelated to premature labor, and over the last 24 hours the pain had become persistent and severe. An ultrasound in the emergency room had revealed a normal pregnancy, but large amounts of fluid were noted within the abdominal cavity. The Radiologist suspected the fluid was blood, although he had no clue as to the source.

I reviewed the findings and possible causes with Shelley and her nervous husband and other family members in attendance. Since the pregnancy was normal in all other aspects, I reassured them that the cause had to be outside of the uterus, and its identification and management should have no effect on the baby. Thus reassured, Shelley gave her permission to proceed with a surgical examination of her abdomen, begging me to take all necessary precautions to ensure the health of her unborn.

She was taken to the operating room, properly sedated, blood transfusion initiated, and with a general surgeon as an assistant (still not knowing the cause of the bleeding) I proceed to carefully open the abdomen. The shocking image I saw upon entering this woman's 22-week pregnant abdomen is still with me. There was a large amount of free blood which was cleared out, and the uterus, which at this point in the pregnancy filled the abdominal cavity from her pelvis up to half way between the belly button and the tip of the sternum, came into view. But instead of a healthy red muscular uterine wall protecting and nurturing the growing and developing baby, I found myself staring thru a thin transparent membrane – a large window – enclosing a fluid filled sac within which a 22-week-old fetus was visibly moving about. For about a 6-inch diameter circle there was no uterine wall at all, only the thin amniotic sac was keeping the fetus from falling out into the abdomen. And the entire edge of the defect was slowly and continuously seeping blood. At that point the assistant surgeon made a flippant comment about how it appeared the problem was going to be mine after all[1].

What to do. The simplest solution would have been to deliver the baby and repair the uterus, but the pregnancy was nowhere close to the point that would have given the baby a chance at survival. And the widespread bleeding had no available solution for repair or containment, nor would the defective uterus be able to continue allowing the baby to develop for the necessary duration before a safe delivery could be undertaken.

I had a phone brought into the operating room, and a call placed to our level-3 care facility, about 150 miles distant, to see if I could transfer the patient into more capable and experienced hands. The physician on call listened to the story, asked appropriate questions about the situation, and then respectfully declined the transfer, as he felt the patient was medically unstable, and didn't see how they could offer care beyond what was available at my facility and within my capabilities. I also consulted with one of my colleagues at home to see if he had any thoughts or advice, and his only relevant comment was that he was glad I was the one on call.

Again, what to do.

I hesitated in making what was obviously becoming the inevitable decision. In similar cases, medically and legally the health and life of the mother takes precedence over that of the fetus, although if the pregnancy is far enough along for fetal survival, that point can be vigorously and often successfully argued by the mother.

During my residency training one of the most difficult cases I witnessed involved an absolutely delightful 38-year-old woman who had been

---

[1] Thankfully he remained alongside to provide help as needed.

diagnosed at 16 weeks in her first pregnancy with an invasive and aggressive appearing cervical cancer. This was actually her fourth pregnancy, but the first three had ended with miscarriages due to unknown causes. This one was a girl, and she had made it further along than her predecessors, and it looked promising for a term, healthy delivery, which the excited and expectant mother was eagerly anticipating.

Until the cervical cancer diagnosis.

Given the aggressive appearance of the malignancy, the Oncologist[1] had recommended immediate radical hysterectomy – that is, complete removal of the uterus, containing the healthy pregnancy, followed by radiation therapy. The patient had asked for a delay until the baby could be safely delivered, which the Perinatologist[2] had placed at 32 weeks of gestation, four months hence. The patient decided to wait an additional two weeks, giving her baby a chance at a healthy and intact survival. She made it to the threshold, delivered a healthy baby girl, and at the time of the cesarean the hysterectomy was carried out[3]. No doubt due to the large blood supply feeding the advanced pregnancy, she suffered massive bleeding in spite of the precautions and expertise present. During the surgery and ongoing transfusions her case was complicated by extensive clotting defects, she suffered a stroke, and while she survived the procedure, she never left the intensive care unit, and died less than a month later, with her newborn still in the nursery. This wonderful and

---

[1] Oncologist: cancer specialist. A subspecialty would be Gynecologic Oncologist, dealing only with cancer in women.
[2] Perinatologist: specialist in managing complicated pregnancies.
[3] In anticipation of the major surgery to immediately follow the delivery, the Cesarean was carried out under general anesthesia. Therefore, the patient was not awake to see or hold her baby at birth.

excited first-time mother passed away without ever recovering significant consciousness, and never having held her creation. In retrospect, the cancer turned out to be an advanced grade-3, stage-3 malignancy, with a poor long-term prognosis.

I can only hope that the little girl grew up to be a mature, successful woman, always mindful of the ultimate sacrifice that her mother made to ensure her healthy survival.

* * *

Shelley's case was out of options. I changed out of my blood-stained surgical garb and left my assistant to keep an eye on the situation during my absence. I wanted to personally speak with the husband and family members before obtaining their consent for what needed to be done. I answered their questions, explained why their various suggestions could not be implemented, and watched as the group collectively broke down in tears and sobs. Returning to the operating room, the uterus was opened and the tiny but perfectly formed baby delivered to the care of a pediatrician. This physician did not undertake any efforts at keeping the baby alive, as it was not even able to make sounds with its premature lungs, and the eyes were still fused shut. It quietly expired in a few minutes. With the pregnancy out of the way, it was possible to repair the defect in the uterus, closing the edges and at the same time stopping the bleeding. The rest of Shelley's abdomen was cleared of blood and clots, and the surgery completed.

All that remained was dealing with the distraught patient coming out of anesthesia and shortly wondering why her pregnancy, previously described as normal and healthy, was no longer there. I had about 30 minutes to prepare to deal with her, but 30 days would not have been adequate.

The lining of the uterus is actually made up of three layers. The deepest layer, closest to the interior, is the lush growth, thick with blood vessels, that allows the embryo to attach and grow, and in the case of an unsuccessful conception, is shed during the next period. It lays upon a thin layer – the Basal Layer – that is active in building everything back up after a cycle. This intermediate layer is also perfused with blood vessels, but is more muscular, and designed to stop the bleeding when the deep layer is shed, or, in the case of pregnancy, after separation of the placenta after delivery. The outer most layer is extensive muscle tissue, able to stretch remarkably during pregnancy and squeeze out a term baby.

During menstrual bleeding, after childbirth, or during a surgical clearing of the uterus, the deep layer is readily lost, and subsequently replaced by the Basal Layer, which is usually retained. The Basal Layer can also be lost with vigorous scraping during a D&C, or from repeated implantations of a placenta at the same site. While these cases can cause excessive bleeding, if the Basal Layer loss is small and localized it will again be successfully repaired by the body. If, however, large sections of the Basal Layer are lost, there can be no repair, and the deep lush layer is not reproduced, and instead a permanent scar is formed at the site. This can occur during a vigorous D&C by someone who is trying to remove some inaccessible fragment of tissue from a miscarriage, or in the case of inexperience, as the scraping digs deeper into the lining. In this scenario, the bleeding actually increases, giving the impression that something is left behind, leading to more scraping. And the easiest segment of the uterus to manually scrape is the front, facing the mother's abdomen. And so, in inexperienced hands, the sharp blade is repeatedly passed over the same area, digging deeper and deeper into the lining, creating a scar. If in a future pregnancy the placenta comes to impinge upon or cover the resulting scar, it can eat into and invade the muscle layer, with a risk of rupture during the pregnancy[1]. Even without the placenta complicating the picture, as the uterus grows, this area, again being a scar, stretches very poorly, so there is a risk that it will eventually separate, creating the window that I saw when I first gazed upon Shelley's uterus.

* * *

There is an addendum to the story.

With such a large defect repair in the uterus (basically a vertical repair almost half-way around the organ) during her follow-up visit I strongly advised Shelley to avoid a future pregnancy. Her only options, in my opinion at the time, outside of adoption, were surrogacy[2]. If she ever did find herself pregnant, I hoped that she would ensure care in the hands of a specialist, at a facility that could deal emergently with a uterine rupture during pregnancy.

I never saw Shelley again, as she moved to another community. About two years later I received a letter in the mail containing a picture of a darling newborn, and a note. Shelley did get pregnant, followed my advice and received care from a specialist. And incredibly, her scarred uterus carried that baby to term and allowed an uncomplicated cesarean delivery. I'm glad she did well elsewhere, as having seen the extent of that defect, I'm not sure I could have handled the stress for that many months.

---

[1] For the curious, this is termed a 'Placenta Accreta'.
[2] An IVF type procedure, but having another woman carry the baby to term.

One Pair to Two Pair to Three of a kind to a Full House

I clearly recall my professor in Embryology class stating that the female breast is nothing more than "glorified sweat glands". I found the statement dismissive, and suspected that most of my classmates, male and female, also felt the same. Somewhat later it was revealed that the breast tissue of men and women are quite similar[1], with the biggest difference being the size and number of secreting glands, with the female breast structure defined by the presence of the female hormone Estrogen[2]. The size of the adult female breast is also determined by the deposition of fat tissue around the secreting glands, with the number of glands being rather constant across women with different breast sizes. And of course, during pregnancy these glands markedly enlarge in anticipation of the nutritional needs of the newborn.

And then there are the examples that go awry.

* * *

Kaitlen was a 22-year-old first time mom, with an uncomplicated medical history, and a routine pregnancy and delivery. She had successfully started breast feeding before being dismissed home. She was scheduled for a routine follow-up visit at six weeks, but called for an appointment one week after going home. Seems she was experiencing significant underarm

---

[1] Because of the similarity, men can also be diagnosed with breast cancer. Because of the reduced size and number of breast glands, and absence of Estrogen, the incidence in men is about one in ten that of women, everything else being equal.
[2] Estrogen, in all of its forms. Fat storage cells secrete a hormone that is similar to Estrogen, which is why universally, obese individuals, male or female, tend to develop prominent breasts.

103

pain and odor. Knowing she could be suffering from an infected sweat gland, or atypical breast infection, I had her come in at the end of the day.

Examination in the office was rather remarkable. Her breasts were not particularly tender, and there were no well-defined red areas, the hallmarks of breast infection. Examination of her underarms revealed large, somewhat lumpy and tender masses on both sides. These were so pronounced that Kaitlen could not lower her arms to her sides.

While the diagnosis was suspected at this point, closer examination clinched it. Her underarms had numerous scattered, small pigmented spots, resembling freckles, which she insisted had appeared after her delivery. What was remarkable was that each freckle was secreting a tiny, milky drop of fluid, And the secretions would become a tiny flow if pressure was applied to the associated underarm lump. In one thunderclap moment, the diagnosis was established and my Embryology professor was vindicated.

The results were reviewed with the incredulous patient. It would appear that she was blessed, or cursed as the case may be, with extra breasts along the upper portion of her milk line. These breasts did not have associated nipples, having regressed to a more primitive form, as found in mammals such as Kangaroos, whose newborns get nutrition by licking milk secreted from the skin overlying the mother's breast tissues.

Given the unusual location, and the inability to drain the milk production, Kaitlen's extra breasts were at significant risk of developing a nasty infection, the last thing she needed at this point in her life[1].

---

[1] Any extra breast is also at risk of developing breast cancer. Another consideration in recommending removal.

She was referred to a surgical specialist (this procedure being outside of my expertise), the extra tissues were removed, and she was able to continue nursing her newborn, and comfortably resting her arms at her side while doing so. She also earned a spot in my collection of unusual patients, although I kept that honor to myself.

* * *

Medically, most conditions having to do with the breast have a suffix based on 'Mastos', which is Greek for 'breast'. Thus, we have Gynecomastia (female breast[1]), Mastitis (infection of the breast), and Polymastia (more than two breasts). The medical root term for the nipple is based on the Greek word 'Thilia'. An example is Polythelia – more than two nipples.

* * *

In the developing fetus the breast tissue is laid down along a line that runs roughly from the outer edge of the chest near the armpit to the inner crease of the thigh with the groin. Many mammals develop multiple nipples and associated breasts along this line, but humans, needing to typically feed only one offspring at a time, only develop one breast structure on each side, in the location we have come to expect. This line is called, simply enough, the Milk Line, and in the developing fetus it is the Mammary Ridge.

While we have come to expect adult females to be blessed with two breasts bearing one nipple each, it is surprising how many women have extras – from small, pigmented skin lesions, representing primitive nipples, to

---

[1] Usually used to denote inappropriate breast development.

fully formed and complete extra breasts[1]. In most cases the extra tissue is represented by an underdeveloped nipple, which may appear, at a casual glance, as a freckle or mole[2]. This darkened skin region, if it lies along the mammary ridge, very likely represents an extra nipple, and is present in up to one out of every six women[3]. It is frequently not properly identified, even by family physicians, although during puberty many of them will darken and may even enlarge. These changes lead one to worry about melanoma and skin cancer, and so the astute physician then removes the lesion and the truth comes out a week later with the pathology report. I was guilty of this myself on a number of occasions, and even in cases where the location and appearance were consistent with an extra nipple, the lesion was removed due to concerns that a skin abnormality may have been present.

In more advanced cases the extra breast is represented by a small areola[4] surrounding a small, raised bump: the nipple. Even more rare are the cases with thickening of the underlying skin tissues in a representation of a complete breasts. Following pregnancy these tissues will often thicken further and secrete milk during nursing[5]. While breast development usually follows nipple development, in very rare cases one can see a developed and functioning breast without an overlying nipple.

---

[1] I limit the discussion to adult females because of my specialty, but everything having to do with the breast is equally applicable to the adult male.
[2] In men the simpler form of an extra breast is often represented by a tight patch of hair.
[3] For examples of polythelia and polymastia, see plates 13 and 14, A&B.
[4] The dark skin ring surrounding a normal nipple.
[5] There are reported cases of females with extra breasts and nipples able to support feeding their babies. Some of these cases had the extra breasts outside of the milk line. An extreme case involved a lactating breast on the outside of the upper thigh.

The normal nipple represents a focal point where all of the milk ducts converge at a common exit, giving the baby a simple means of obtaining nutrition. When absent, it would appear that each gland unit develops its own path to the skin surface, as the case with Kaitlen demonstrated. Why each duct exit had a pigmented area (a freckle, so to speak) around it has never been explained.

Glorified sweat glands, indeed.

The Leak & The Plumber

Carol was a 30-year-old patient presenting with her second pregnancy. Her first pregnancy (unexpected and dreaded) and delivery were uncomplicated, although at the time she was involved in a very abusive relationship. Six years later she found herself pregnant again, this time while in a loving and caring relationship, and was excitedly looking forward to the delivery. Given her history I expected this pregnancy to also be uncomplicated, and so it was, until a casual call one morning, at around 14-weeks of gestation. It seemed Carol had experienced some vaginal leakage, primarily clear fluid, described as a couple tablespoon equivalent, with some blood tinging. She had intercourse 48 hours prior, and didn't think much of it as her next appointment was within the week, but her husband convinced her to call. No other complaints, and I tended to agree that it probably was related to the sexual activity and not a concern, but I had her come in at the end of day for an ultrasound. It was all so routine that her husband was not in attendance. The ultrasound however, immediately changed the situation.

The fetus was appropriately sized, with a regular heartbeat, but there was a complete absence of amniotic fluid. Where a normal 14-week gestation is literally floating in a copious volume of fluid, this fetus was squeezed on all sides by the uterus and placenta. Further examination revealed the cervix to be thick and closed, and the reason for the premature rupture was never apparent, but I repeatedly reassured the now terrified mother that it had nothing to do with any preceding activity on her part.

By this point Carol was beet red and the tears were freely flowing. She managed to call her husband to come to the office for support and to review the situation.

* * *

Premature rupture of the membranes is usually related to labor, but spontaneously in early pregnancy the reason is usually impossible to identify. Infection is the most commonly accepted cause, but in a large number of cases the infection follows the rupture, as a result and not the cause. A defect in the membranes is sometimes suggested, but again there is no evidence. After the age of viability[1], currently around 23-24 weeks of gestation, there are a number of options, such as expectant management for a few days, to allow the associated stress to mature the baby while antibiotics are given a chance to keep infections at bay. One can also deliver the baby, either by induction or Cesarean. But at 14 weeks of gestation viability is a long way off, and even if the pregnancy were to continue, the lack of amniotic fluid will result in a number of serious consequences for the developing fetus. These can range from failure to develop the lungs (lethal at birth), to arm or leg development failures, loss of fingers or toes, or entire hands and feet, and facial abnormalities, all due to the direct pressure from the wall of the uterus. The pregnancy may also be lost due to pressure on the unprotected umbilical cord.

And the dragon of infection is always just around the corner, waiting to lunge at the first opportunity.

Lab results did not demonstrate any evidence of infection, and I again found myself in a difficult situation, with a mother begging for all

---

[1] Plate-12B is an extreme example of prematurity.

measures to be taken to save her pregnancy. The textbook recommendation for this scenario is immediate delivery to protect the mother, and my partner also recommended that I proceed with standard recommendations.

My next step was to consult a Perinatologist[1], who also recommended ending the pregnancy in order to protect the mother. However, two issues stood in the way: our local hospital would not allow any procedure that even hinted at termination, regardless of indication, and Carol was not about to allow herself to be transferred for the procedure. Seeing the healthy heartbeat of the fetus and no evidence of infection, and reviewing the risks, which she readily accepted, I offered the option to continue the pregnancy with close observation. She was instructed to check her temperature twice a day and report the results, and I had her come in for another blood test in three days, and an ultrasound in one week. I fully expected the baby to shortly expire, or labor to ensue and force the decision.

Carol's status remained unchanged. Her next ultrasound again confirmed the lack of fluid, but surprisingly, appropriate growth in the fetus, who continued to demonstrate a regular heartbeat. My partner continued to recommend a termination to protect the mother as he did not see any potential good outcome. But with the situation stable I allowed the routine to continue. And so it did, until 16 weeks, when the ultrasound showed a sliver of fluid surrounding the fetus, who for the first time in two weeks demonstrated some movement. And one week later the sliver had grown measurably, and continued to increase, until at 20-weeks of gestation the fluid collection appeared normal. Carol experienced no further loss of fluid and there were never any signs of infection. Her visits

---

[1] Perinatologist: a specialist in managing high-risk pregnancies.

were spaced out, her temperature checks reduced to once a day, and then every other day. And at 26 weeks, with the fetus appearing normal, active, and surrounded by a normal volume of fluid, and the mother reporting regular movements, I transferred Carol back into a normal pregnancy category. All that remained to be seen were the consequences of weeks of no fluid on the baby's development.

Thus, the pregnancy continued until 39 weeks, at which point Carol called complaining of a sudden loss of fluid again. This time it was obviously due to labor, and shortly afterwards she delivered a perfectly healthy and adorably normal little girl, who possessed all of her arms and legs, an appropriate number of fingers and toes, and her howls of protest at delivery left no doubt as to the adequacy of her lungs.

* * *

My partner reserved comments, knowing the results spoke for themselves, and he never brought it up again.

Afterwards, the Perinatologist, when advised of the outcome, commented that there are "no plumbers in the uterus" and leaks do not stop leaking. He further hinted that the Ultrasonographer must have been mistaken, for ruptured membranes do not heal spontaneously.

But I was the one doing all of the ultrasound examinations, and the evidence was undeniable.

Twins

Twin pregnancies always carried a special joy when they showed up in my practice[1]. Some physicians dread the discovery in new obstetrical patients, as these patients are automatically classified as high-risk pregnancies, necessitating a lot of work and sleepless nights, as well as increased liability. I knew a number of physicians that would immediately refer these patients to high-risk specialists. Working as a solo practitioner in a small town in the middle of the state, I did not have that luxury, without creating tremendous inconvenience to the patients, for the nearest specialist were about two hours driving distance. In addition, I was fortunate in having had extensive experience in my training dealing with what are called 'high order' pregnancies. As a resident physician I was deeply involved in the care of triplets and one set of quadruplets. I was doubly fortunate to be asked to assist in the delivery of the latter – cesarean of course – and have never experienced such a sight. There was a team attending to the mother (who was conscious but numb from the waist down) consisting of two experienced obstetricians, one very nervous resident physician, one anesthesiologist, one surgical nurse, one scrub nurse, one float nurse, and somewhere buried within the drapes and the crowd, an expectant father who was also numb, but unrelated to anesthesia. Attending to each expectant newborn was a team consisting of a skilled neonatal nurse and a pediatrician. My job was to hold retractors, clear out what seemed like endless gallons of blood and amniotic fluid with a quarter inch suction tip, and hand carry each newborn over to the respective station, gently set it down on a sterile sheet, and hustle back to the operating theater without contaminating myself. Each time I carried out my duties with one of the babies I was under the scrutiny of the float nurse, whose sole mission in life was to

---

[1] Or properly, 'multiple gestations'. If greater than two, it would be 'high order pregnancies'.

catch me contaminating something and to announce it to the world with a roar and a bellow, and then smirk while I was yelled at by the surgical team, and cursed for being absent while re-gloving, or covering whatever had been contaminated. My mission in turn was to ensure I didn't drop any babies, and to disappoint the float nurse, both of which I managed to accomplish.

When the uterus was opened there was a massive gush of amniotic fluid with the rupturing of the sacs, and fetal arms & legs appeared at random thru the incision. As each cord was clamped and the fetus handed off, there was the expectant wait for the first cry. Even though these babies were only about 31-weeks along at the time of delivery (versus the normal 37 to 42 weeks for term singletons), two of them cried right away and one took a bit of encouragement before screaming in protest at the insult. The fourth little guy took his time, giving all of us apprehension, but he finally added his voice to the chorus. I suspect even today he is causing his parents grief.

* * *

One of the first obstetrical patients I acquired as a private physician was a very young lady whom I first spied sitting in the waiting area, somewhat obese, short in stature, and playing with a doll. I incredulously asked the staff if she was the new obstetrical patient, and her age, for she looked nine or ten. Turns out Chloe was actually twelve, and accompanied by her mother. And the ultimate joke on all of us was the finding that not only was Chloe already pregnant at about 10-weeks of gestation, but that she was carrying twins. Now I knew with certainty that somewhere out there was a male who had engaged in sexual activity with a 12-year-old child. And it turned out the perpetrator (the term 'rapist' would be equally valid) was actually sixteen, and well known to the family. And the family wasn't interested in pursuing charges, and the police (who were contacted discretely, preserving the patient's privacy) were also not interested in pursuing charges. So much for the excitement of my first set of twins in private practice. After a number of visits during which it became obvious that the pregnancy would proceed normally to conclusion, I asked Chloe's mother about plans after delivery. Chloe herself had no participation in the conversations, and I suspected it was outside her sphere of interest. Her mother related their plan to adopt out the twins, a decision I considered appropriate and wise.

The pregnancy proceeded uneventfully, even given the mother's age. What was disappointing was the complete lack of interest on the part of Chloe. She continued to show more fascination with her toys, and continued to be disinterested in the pregnancy. The numerous ultrasounds and discussions about the pregnancy failed to trigger any interest, and my attempts to engage her in conversation and discussion were consistently ignored. And soon, the pregnancy, which remained surprisingly uncomplicated, reached its conclusion, and two healthy baby girls were delivered, about four weeks early, but vigorous and able to go home with their mother in a few days. I was surprised that no one had visited regarding the adoption or made inquiries, and that's when Chloe's mother related the latest turn of events. It appeared that Chloe's father was of Native American descent, making Chloe one-half, and the babies one-fourth Native American. And in the United States the Native American tribe gets first pick on babies that are one-eighth or more of tribal heritage, and due to be adopted. And this particular tribe had laid claim to the twins at the last minute, planning on placing them with a single mother, living on a reservation with two small children. And Chloe's mother had decided that she couldn't allow that to happen, and would take the babies home and raise them herself (I wasn't sure of her logic, or how she came to the conclusion that the babies would be better off in her care). I couldn't help but wonder about outcomes, given that she was already responsible for having raised one 12-year-old pregnant girl.

I saw Chloe again at her postpartum visit, attended by the twins and their grandmother. While I've come across a number of young mothers who start out childish and immature, almost universally they show an incredible degree of maturation once the care of the baby becomes their responsibility. They often outgrow the original boyfriend and move on, to the benefit of themselves and the child. This was unfortunately not the case with Chloe, who continued to be distracted and disinterested. And her mother, the primary caregiver, appeared exhausted, overwhelmed, and old beyond her years.

* * *

There's a joke about Obstetricians needing to retire when they start delivering the babies of the babies they have delivered. My next contact with Chloe actually involved one of her daughters, who turned up in my office fifteen years later, distracted and disinterested, playing on her smart phone. She had, at the age of fifteen, a ragged amateurish tattoo of a teardrop next to one eye, numerous other tattoos scattered thru-out, none of which could be called artistic, and a number that were obviously homemade. She had multiple piercings of her face.

And she was pregnant, about nine weeks along.

I suppose there's some consolation in the fact that she got three years further along than her mother.

Rita and Her Boys

I had a number of infertility patients under my care, and had the training to perform a number of procedures to try and assist them in overcoming their difficulties. However, my training did not extend to, nor did our community have the resources for pursuing, in-vitro fertilization, or IVF. In addition, the fact that our hospital was a devout Catholic institution would have resulted in the administration frowning upon many aspects of the procedure. The infertility procedures that I did perform resulted in a number of twins, but I was innocent of inducing higher order pregnancies.

Rita on the other hand, was one of my infertility failures. She was a delightful mid-30's lady, married to a man ten years older, and together they were the definition of small-town humble humility, hard work, and ethical standards. Her only issue was an inability to achieve pregnancy, for reasons that were never clear, as both Rita and her husband were extremely healthy, with appropriate weight and normal laboratory test results. Try as I might, with my training, procedures and prescriptions, instructions, and Rita's dedication to the cause, she never did conceive. They did not have the resources nor comfort level for a try at IVF[1], and approaching 40 for Rita and 50 for her husband, they resigned themselves to attempting adoption. And knowing the long list of waiting couples, most of whom were younger and in better financial condition, they realized that they probably would live out their lives without an occupied nursery.

And then Jamie presented to the emergency room.

---

[1] At the time of these events, IVF was considered an elective procedure, and was generally not covered by insurance.

Jamie was a 19-year-old, single college student, recently sexually active, never having had a Pap smear or pelvic exam, naïve about contraception, and terrified and suspicious of the possibility that she might be pregnant. Her last period was two months previous, and just as she had resigned herself to getting a pregnancy test, she had started bleeding, hence the visit to the emergency room late at night. I was on duty that night when the call came in. By that time the ER staff had performed lab tests and confirmed Jamie's pregnancy. I duly arrived and introduced myself, and one of the first statements from Jamie was a question about the steps necessary to obtain an abortion. I do not take a stand on the procedure, leaving it to the autonomy of the patients and their individual beliefs. As to Jamie's inquiry, I let her know that bleeding in the first trimester was associated with a significant risk of miscarriage, and that scheduling an abortion might be premature. I could tell immediately that Jamie was intelligent and healthy, and she denied any illicit drug use. She didn't even like to drink, and her unprotected sexual activity appeared to be the extent of her bad habits. And on that note, I proceeded with the ultrasound.

It was immediately clear that Jamie was carrying twins, in separate sacs, both with a strong heartbeat and normal fluid volumes. There was some blood behind the placenta, but the heavy bleeding that had brought her into the emergency room appeared to be subsiding, although the risk of a miscarriage was still significant. I casually asked about Jamie's situation, and why an abortion was her first thought. Turned out she was financially struggling, busy with work and school, and terrified at the thought of a pregnancy, and what it would do to her immediate schedule and future plans. And the father of the baby turned out to be literally a one-night affair, and totally out of the picture.

At this point, if the mother is interested in pursuing the pregnancy, there are some medications that can reduce, somewhat, the risk of continued bleeding. It was appropriate to prescribe these, and offer recommendations in an effort to try and minimize further bleeding risks. Not that I was trying to maintain her pregnancy, but only because a miscarriage, especially with twins, can lead to significant loss of blood. An abortion procedure under controlled and stable circumstances is much safer. Jamie accepted the recommendations and was dismissed home with precautions, and a one-week follow-up appointment. I knew she could proceed with the abortion at any time, but was secretly hoping her financial situation would delay the decision. And I started thinking about Rita.

Jamie dutifully showed up at her appointment, still pregnant, and reported that the bleeding had ceased. I would have done an ultrasound at this point on anyone in a similar situation, but in Jamie's case I made sure she could see the babies with their strong and regular heart beats, and made sure the volume on the machine was nice and loud. And I brought up the subject of adoption. Except for being terrified at the thought of a pregnancy, especially with twins, she had never contemplated the idea, but I could see a seed beginning to take root. A bit more encouragement, and another follow-up visit, perhaps a bit sooner than necessary. Again, the ultrasound with the screen turned a bit more towards the patient than normal, the volume a bit louder than usual. And I noted that Jamie was beginning to take more of an interest in what was going on in her body. A bit more information was provided on adoption and some of the financial aid that can be legally provided, and another appointment. And so it went, to the day when she smiled at the babies' movements, and the day she excitedly reported feeling flutters, and finally the day she realized that she really was a mother to be, and started asking questions regarding the babies, and potential adoptive parents.

And it so happened that I knew the perfect couple.

And they met, and they immediately hit it off, and Jamie started outlining a set of rules, most of them routine, but emphasizing her desire to maintain visitation rights afterwards, to which Rita and her husband readily agreed.

And knowing that God would never take things this far only to play out a bitter end, I stopped worrying about Jamie losing the babies.

Jamie delivered at 37 weeks, identical, healthy twin boys. Rita was present at the delivery, and was as excited as any new mom I can ever recall. She had made extensive plans and arrangements, and prepared a nursery well stocked with all of the amenities necessary to take care of two healthy newborns.

Her biggest regret was the anticipation of bottle feeding. She had actually inquired about medications and techniques to force milk production in a non-pregnant female. It can be done, but the regimen carries significant risks, more so as the woman ages, and with her husband's understanding and support I talked her out of it. The babies went home with their new family, and even now, every Christmas, I receive a card from Rita with an updated picture, and a list of milestones and plans for the year. The boys have done well, are due to graduate, and both are looking forward to college and agricultural degrees so they can take over their father's business.

And when I look at the pictures in the card, I also think of Jamie, the sweet, scared young college student, terrified at the thought of pregnancy and yet brave beyond her years, bringing such priceless joy into the lives of complete strangers. I have lost contact with her, but will always wish her well.

* * *

There are basically three ways a pregnancy can become complicated with multiple gestations. The first is artificial, caused by ovarian stimulation, or during a form of infertility treatment commonly known as 'in vitro fertilization', IVF, or 'test tube pregnancy'. To ensure success, often more than one egg is introduced into the uterus. As luck would have it, sometimes all of them adhere and grow. In the early days of IVF, when the technique was more in line with shotguns and sledge hammers, many eggs would be introduced. This occasionally resulted in disastrous high order pregnancies, sometimes up to a dozen implantations. There's no way the human body can carry such a load, so these unfortunate cases ended up being a total loss, with its attendant emotional toll. The highest successful high order pregnancy that resulted in live babies has been eight. I cannot imagine the complications and costs associated with this number. Nowadays, with more refined techniques, it's unusual to see more than two or three fertilized eggs being inserted. Occasionally, they all take off, and as luck would have it, sometimes you have to deal with the added complication of spontaneous splitting in the midst of all this. Even with the more conservative approach we find that assisted reproduction is still responsible for one-third of all twins, and three-quarters of all triplets.

The other way a multiple pregnancy can come about is thru a couple of natural processes. The first of these involves the release of more than one egg during a cycle, with subsequent fertilization and implantation of each. This natural process is referred to as dizogotic twinning, and the result is fraternal twins. Since each egg represents a unique individual, these twins can be the same or different sex, and have similar, but not identical DNA. Therefore, their similarity is along the lines of siblings. And of course, human sexuality being what it is, there is at least one documented case of a woman giving birth to twins of different races. It would appear that the month her body ovulated two eggs, she decided to have sex with different men within the 48-hour window of fertilization opportunity. One can only hope that she wasn't seriously involved with either, for this is one evidence of infidelity that would be hard to explain away.

There are a number of correlations with dizygotic twins. There appear to be hereditary factors, as well as racial factors and age factors at work. The risk of having dizygotic twins varies from a low of four to five per thousand in Japanese women, to 10-12 per thousand in parts of India, to a high of 20-22 in parts of Africa. The underlying cause in at least some of these African populations is suspected to be due to high consumption of yams, which contain an ovarian hormone-like compound[1]. The risk of having dizygotic twins also increases as the woman ages, generally doubling after the age of 35. Again, the underlying mechanism is unknown, but possibly due to the increased levels of ovarian stimulating hormones that are normally seen in older women.

---

[1] Forget any thoughts of increasing fertility by chomping on yams. The consumption has to be consistent, inordinate and sustained. Even then the association is only suspected.

In all cases, when I refer to the rate of twins, the number is the live birth rate. The conception rate is significantly higher when one considers the fact that many pregnancies that start out as twins will lose one or both at some point before delivery. The risk of a loss during a pregnancy with twins is almost four times that of a singleton pregnancy, all else being the same. Rarely, the loss of one twin is identified at the time of delivery, especially if it occurs before about 12-14 weeks of gestation[1]. These lost twins present as a thin, flat outline of a fetus, usually pressed against the amniotic membranes, with the length roughly corresponding to the gestational age at the time of the loss.

* * *

The other form of natural twining is called monozygotic, resulting in identical twins. This results from a single egg, splitting and separating into two after fertilization. Since the twins are from the same ovum, they are always the same sex, and have identical DNA. The risk of this form of twinning is the same across all human populations, at about three per 1000 live births (actually one out of every 285 live births).

Of course, any process that causes twins can also lead to triplets or more, but statistically, the numbers begin to pale. The chance of spontaneous identical triplets should be three per million, but in reality, it is about half of that or less, due to the higher risk of early pregnancy loss. One can also see triplets that are a combination of identical and paternal twining. This process is usually responsible for higher order spontaneous pregnancies, with the most recent example being a case of spontaneous quintuplets in 2016 in Australia, made up of one boy and four girls.

---

[1] See Plate-6A.

The first recorded case of surviving identical spontaneous quintuplets were five girls born in Canada in 1934. Their life story is a sad read in greed and corruption[1].

Paternal or dizygotic twins, being individuals, have their own placenta and amniotic sac, and rarely suffer from connections between their circulations during development. Identical twins however, have a number of issues and complications, unique to their origins. We first have to look at those origins.

Monozygotic twins, as previously noted, begin life as a single fertilized egg. Within twelve hours of fertilization the egg divides, and each resulting cell in turn continues to regularly divide until a ball of cells is formed. At this point the cells begin to show signs of specialization, first forming the precursor of the placenta, then the amniotic sac, and finally, from a nondescript small clump of cells in a corner, the future fetus. What leads the cell mass to occasionally split off into twins is unknown, but the timing can create some interesting results and unusual complications, for once the cells have begun specialization, there is no going back. If the split occurs before the zygote has differentiated, that is up to six days after fertilization, each egg half will develop its own sac and placenta, and the pregnancy will be no more complicated than dizygotic twins[2]. If the split occurs during the first stages of differentiation, day seven thru nine, the twins will have a common placenta, but separate sacs. This frequently leads to circulation connections between the twins. If the connections are minor, or involve veins with their low-pressure blood flow, there are usually no significant complications. But if the connection is arterial, with high pressure flow, there's a risk that one fetus will begin to pump its

---

[1] See *We Were Five*, by James Brough; Simon and Schuster (1965).
[2] These are labeled 'dichorionic-diamniotic' twins.

blood into its twin. This can lead to differences in rates of growth, although the developing fetuses have an amazing ability to compensate for this shift in blood volume.

The worst case is a connection between one fetus's arterial system and the twin's venous system. Then the high-pressure differential will cause a continual flow of blood in one direction, leading to a condition called 'twin-twin transfusion'. The donor twin will end up severely anemic, and may die before birth, while the recipient will be overloaded with blood and at risk of heart failure. Interestingly, if born alive, the donor twin, while significantly smaller, anemic and stressed, does much better than the recipient.

Splitting of the cell mass between days 10-12 with differentiation farther along will result in twins that share placenta and amniotic sac[1]. They reside in the same volume of space, and can hold hands, hug, and dance around each other. Besides the risks of twin-twin transfusion, these twins have the added risk of cord entanglement, as they move and twist around each other. Look up any picture of a newborn and its placenta, and you will see the cord has twists along its entire length. Each twist represents a turn that the fetus made, that wasn't canceled by a return twist[2]. With twins in the same sac, each twist of the umbilical cord could potentially be a twist around the other twin's cord, with the risk for strangulation of one or both. Before the age of viability there's nothing to be done. Restricting the mother's activity has no bearing, and the pregnancy is

---

[1] These are labeled Mono-chorionic, mono-amniotic, or 'mono-mono' twins, in the language of the trade.

[2] Do cords of babies in the northern hemisphere twist opposite those of babies carried in the southern hemisphere? The answer is 'no' since I've seen cords twisted both ways, and in about equal ratios, and almost all of my patients were northern hemisphere dwellers. Does the direction of the cord twist say something about the mothers or baby's handedness? No, for the same reason.

managed as any other twin gestation. The management decisions become an issue after the age of viability, which is currently around 24 weeks of gestation.

* * *

I received a call one afternoon from a colleague in an adjoining community. An obstetrical patient, who was at around the mid-point of her pregnancy, had come into the office for a routine visit, but they were unable to detect any fetal heart tones. And of course, she was too early in the pregnancy to feel the movements of the baby. Knowing the mother's apprehension, I had her drive down to the office for an ultrasound evaluation that day[1].

Upon her arrival, after the necessary paperwork and the introductions were completed, a brief ultrasound was undertaken. It quickly demonstrated a pregnancy at 20-weeks' gestation, consistent with her dates, and normal except for absent fetal heart activity. The fetus had succumbed, and since none of the signs of remote demise were present[2], it was probably something that had occurred within the past 24 hours, for unknown reasons[3]. It took some time to console the mother, even with

---

[1] While pregnancy ultrasounds are routine nowadays and usually performed by a tech, at the time of this incident in rural communities, it was reserved for high risk or complicated pregnancies. My training allowed me to do my own, which was one of the more pleasant aspects of my practice.

[2] Decrease in fluid, loss of contrast in the fetus on ultrasound, and other signs depending on how long ago the fetus died.

[3] Loss of a pregnancy is actually rather common in the first trimester and associated with chromosomal or developmental abnormalities in a majority of cases, and a low risk of recurrence unless it is repetitive. Miscarriage risk rapidly tapers off thereafter. Fetal demise is unusual after 16 weeks, and warrants investigation as to the cause, and means of prevention for the next pregnancy, for the recurrence risk is significant.

her premonition of bad news. The recommendation was admission and induction of labor, for given the advanced state of the pregnancy, surgical options were quite risky.

Over the next 24 hours the medications performed their tasks, and the mother went into labor, which was thankfully rapid, and resulted in delivery of an intact, size appropriate and normal appearing fetus, consistent with the ultrasound findings. What wasn't seen on the ultrasound was the cause of the demise, which was suddenly and painfully obvious. The pregnancy had started out as monozygotic twins, and the split had occurred late, resulting in a monochorionic, monoamniotic pregnancy. Early in the pregnancy, the umbilical cords had become entwined, resulting in the death of one fetus, which from appearance was around 10-weeks of gestation. The second twin had survived the insult, and continued to grow, while the lost twin had collapsed into a fibrous mass, and its umbilical cord had taken on the characteristics of a strong string, a strong string tied around the cord of the survivor. And in the final tragedy, as the surviving twin continued to grow and develop, and its umbilical cord thickened, the tangle of these cords tightened until the second twin succumbed also[1].

* * *

The only other case of mono-mono twins that came across my practice involved a young mother on her third pregnancy. At the time of her ultrasound, it was immediately obvious that Mary was carrying twins, they were obviously boys, and the lack of a membrane between them confirmed their monozygotic origins. The excitement of the moment was tempered by the knowledge that this would be an especially complicated

---

[1] See Plate-6B.

pregnancy, with a significant risk of loss of both twins at some point. With the shocked mother and father calming down somewhat, I decided to hold off on the bad news, and sent them on their way.

With the diagnosis confirmed at the second ultrasound, around 16 weeks of gestation, I explained to Mary and her husband the potential complications of her pregnancy, and reviewed management options. When I explained my recommendations, Mary readily agreed, although her husband was somewhat reluctant in the beginning. The sacrifice involved can only be appreciated when one realizes that I suggested she enter a level-3 care facility[1], once she successfully reached 24-25 weeks of gestation (the age of viability), and remain there on continuous monitoring until delivery could be safely undertaken, or the need arose for an emergency delivery, in case one or both babies began showing signs of distress.

From experience I have concluded that with pregnant patients, I could recommend hanging upside down from a closet rod for days on end, and most of the patients would comply, if it means a healthy pregnancy and outcome. And Mary was a perfect example, for she readily agreed to the burdensome recommendations, even taking into consideration the inconvenience of the distance from home, the discomfort of being on bed rest for up to three months, even while she left her other two children behind.

The next hurtle was convincing the insurance company.

---

[1] The nearest facility was 150 miles from our community. A level-3 facility is able to provide immediate care for extremely premature babies, and has staff on hand 24-hours a day to perform immediate emergency cesarean deliveries.

Non-physicians do not realize the amount of paperwork involved in providing medical care. With complicated patients, it's not unusual to spend one hour on paperwork and management decisions for every hour spent face to face with the patient. And so began my joust with Mary's insurance carrier. The cost of continuous monitoring for three months, in a high-level care facility, is enormous. And so, the insurance company fought for a less costly alternative. Their recommended alternatives included monitoring at our level-2 facility – potentially pointless, since for 12 hours out of every 24, and on weekends, when the staff was not in house, the time necessary to perform an emergent cesarean could be up to 30 minutes. In addition, our facility couldn't handle premature babies at less than 30-32 weeks of gestation, which meant the younger, weaker, and sicker babies would have to be transported immediately after birth, a terrible stressor for the newborn, on top of everything else.

Finally, after many discussions with the adjusters over the phone, I prevailed, and the monitoring was approved. Now we just had to hope that Mary made it to 24-weeks of gestation age without a disaster.

And so, she did. And on the appointed day, she bid goodbye to her other children and traveled to the concrete and stone edifice, checked herself in, was put in a bed with tight belts and large disks placed on her already impressive abdomen. These belts, which typically leave marks after a few hours, were necessary to allow continuous remote monitoring of the heartbeat of the twins, and would remain on her 24 hours a day, even while in the bathroom. And every week I received an update, showing how things were progressing, and how well the twins were doing. Mary herself was a pillar of strength, and in spite of the misery, never once uttered a complaint. Thus, things progressed, until the day at around 32 weeks of gestation, when suddenly one of the two heartbeats took a steep dive, and remained at less than half the normal rate, a sure sign of a pending catastrophe. Fortunately, the monitoring system worked, the cesarean was undertaken expeditiously, and two healthy and somewhat diminutive little boys were delivered. Both expressed their displeasure with typical vigor and were whisked off to the nursery, where they would remain for about two months, before being sent home to the care of that wonderful mother, willing to sacrifice every comfort and convenience for the sake of her babies[1].

I saw Mary and her twins periodically, when she would bring them in to see their pediatrician, whose office was next door. Mary would always take the time to stop by my office and brag, if only just a little. And so, I was able to observe as they developed and matured into identical, yet distinctively individual, handsome young men, with blond hair and blue eyes, and typical young men's tendency for mischief. I always wondered if anyone ever sat them down and truly explained to them what their mother went thru to bring them both into this world. And I always wondered what the accountants at the insurance company would say to the boys to justify their stand on what they believed was adequate and appropriate care.

* * *

Can an egg split after day 11, when embryo differentiation has begun, and proceed to develop successfully? The answer is yes, but fortunately very rarely. Once the embryo itself has begun differentiation, any complete splitting will likely result in the loss of pregnancy, since each embryo will leave behind something critical with its twin. The usual path to survival is incomplete splitting, which results in conjoined, or 'Siamese' twins.

---

[1] See Plate-7, A & B.

Depending on the conception day and the degree of splitting, the twins may only share distal extremities such as hands or feet, and be surgically separated at birth, or they may share vital organs and resigned to be attached for life[1].

Even more rare, sometimes the twin embryos completely split early in gestation, but shortly afterwards, due to proximity or some other mechanism, reattach. The reattachment can alter the development signals of one or both twins. In the latter cases the pregnancy will probably be lost, but in the former it can leave one twin unable to fully develop, and if the pregnancy reaches the point of delivery, one sees bizarre, but fortunately very rare, cases of babies sporting partial heads, torsos, or extremities, jutting out incongruently from their bodies[2].

One late afternoon, as I was finishing a routine day in the office, I received a rather urgent request from one of our family physicians, who had been taking care of an otherwise normal and healthy pregnant patient, until that day. It seems the mother, presently at 37-weeks of gestation, had come into the office for a routine visit and was noted to be suddenly much larger than expected for her gestational age. She was rather upset, and the office wanted to know if I could evaluate her and discover the reason. Knowing the anxiety present in the expectant woman after anything out of the ordinary, I made arrangements to have her sent over that afternoon, and prepared to perform an ultrasound.

After the usual meet and greet, I started my scan. Immediately it was noted that the volume of fluid surrounding the baby was on the excessive side, but what really stood out was the size of the fetal head. The usual

---

[1] See Plate-10A.
[2] See Plate-10B.

fetal skull measurements, which the machine can use to calculate dates up to 44-weeks of gestational age, were all well off the scale. In addition, the visible structures of the brain appeared abnormal. Knowing the most common cause of an enlarged head of this magnitude is fluid entrapment within the brain, with the attendant risk of permanent brain injury[1], I recommended an urgent cesarean delivery[2]. The mother, still in shock, agreed, and preparations were undertaken, the patient's primary physician, anesthesiologist and pediatrician notified, and the patient prepped and transferred to the operating room.

At delivery, when the uterus was opened and the membranes ruptured, there was a massive gush of fluid, which ran down the operating table and onto and into everyone's shoes. The baby was breech, and the legs, followed by the abdomen and chest were delivered without difficulty. But the head was jammed up inside the uterus, so the incision had to be extended, and extended, and extended some more. The size of the baby's head had everyone amazed, until finally it was completely delivered, and at that point the reason for the abnormality and the attendant drama became clear.

There are certain rare conditions that most Obstetricians only read about, and that are only observed in high end medical facilities, where pregnancies with significant abnormalities are often referred. Looking back, I'm surprised at some of the cases I was personally involved with, and some of the unusual conditions I had to manage during my practice in a small, rural community. And this patient and her newborn are

---

[1] Rarely, tumors.

[2] Cesarean deliveries are classified as scheduled (repeat), unscheduled (for example for failure of labor to progress), urgent, emergent, and the most critical, known as the 'mad dash, splash, and slash' cesarean, reserved for cases when the fetus or mother is at risk of immediate and severe injury or death.

probably at the top of that list. For her pregnancy was complicated by monozygotic twinning, but very, very late in the available window, and markedly incomplete. The baby from the neck down was a perfectly normal male term newborn[1], but the neck, which normally narrows to the base of the skull, was actually broadening as it extended upwards, and the head was comprised of an incomplete fusion of two heads. There was present a single chin, two mouths (moving independently), two malformed noses, one normal appearing eye on each side of the head, with a third cyclopean eye in the middle. And the cranium was massive, no doubt due to the presence of two brains in one skull[2].

And the baby was born alive.

He was transferred to the intensive care nursery where he struggled to breathe, and whimpered weakly out of each mouth, and the normal outer eyes moved independently and blinked. The reason for the struggled breathing was due to a condition called choanal atresia. This occurs when the normal opening in the back of the sinuses doesn't develop, forcing the baby to breathe thru the mouth. And since newborn babies are obligatory nose breathers, the condition has to be surgically addressed right away, to prevent continued struggling and exhaustion.

Shortly the parents, in a state of shock and disbelief, were brought in to see, hold and make decisions regarding their newborn. It's hard to imagine a worse scenario than the one the new mother had just experienced. She started the afternoon with a routine and joyous office visit near the end

---

[1] He did have spina bifida, a not uncommon condition that involves failure of the fusion of the base of the spinal column. Whether this was related to the incomplete twinning or an incidental finding was never determined. These can occur as isolated defects. See plate-9A for a representative example.

[2] This incredibly rare condition is called 'Disprosopus', derived from the Latin for '2-faced'. See Plate-11.

of her uncomplicated pregnancy, with her joy and expectations shattered by a diagnosis of possible abnormality, followed by a diagnosis of serious abnormality requiring immediate cesarean delivery, followed by the birth of a markedly abnormal baby boy. And now, within an hour of delivery, she was presented with the need to make a life and death decision regarding the care of that baby. And she bravely chose to forgo all efforts on the baby's behalf. The newborn was wrapped and kept warm and held by the mother over the next 12 hours, during which the baby progressively became more exhausted, his breathing raspier and irregular, until finally, early the following morning, he quietly expired. By then the mother had depleted her stores of tears, and continued to rock and speak and sing softly to her baby's lifeless form until all warmth had dissipated and the inevitable become obvious. I never saw the mother again after her dismissal, since she followed up with her own physician, but my heart goes out to her, and I can scant imagine her recurrent nightmares of what had transpired, and the terror of what she might have to face with her next pregnancy.

A Tragedy of Twins

One of my worst decision-making cases happened to involve twins during the pregnancy of Julia. She was an unassuming soul, thirty-something years old, with a long history of infertility. My limited attempts had been unsuccessful, and after taking a break for about a year she and her husband chose to pursue in-vitro fertilization. The first two attempts were unsuccessful, and just when they were about to give up completely, they found the resources for one more attempt. And as luck would have it, not only did she conceive, but quickly found out that she was carrying twins. The excitement was blunted somewhat by the review of the risks that are normally reviewed at the beginning, but they seemed to handle it well, and the pregnancy proceeded along expected lines.

Until the call shortly after 21 weeks along in the pregnancy, when with a panic in her voice Julia described increasing cramps followed by a gush of blood-tinged fluid. I forwent the office visit and had her proceed to the hospital, where an ultrasound showed the lower baby with minimal fluid, and a careful vaginal exam revealed her cervix to be widely dilated, with the baby beginning to protrude into the vagina. It was obvious that labor had progressed so far that delivery was inevitable, but still all attempts were undertaken to stabilize the situation.

Over the next few hours, even as her labor abated under the influence of medications and measures, the first baby, still alive, progressed thru the birth canal and delivered. The eyes were still fused, the lungs non-functioning, and the attending Pediatrician did not feel that any attempts at resuscitation were indicated. And the baby quietly expired over the next few minutes. Surprisingly, shortly afterwards there was a complete cessation of labor, and the cervix actually started to close[1]. Unfortunately, the placenta of the delivered baby was still firmly in place, with a length of the attendant umbilical cord dangling within the vagina. And therein began the dilemma. The parents were devastated, and at the same time begging for all measures to be undertaken to prolong the pregnancy beyond 24 weeks, when the remaining fetus would have a chance at survival.

Any Obstetrical textbook, any Obstetrician, any specialist in the field at that time, would have firmly stated that this situation is hopeless, and the only option is to stop all measures and allow the delivery of the second baby. Statistically, there's no chance for continuing the pregnancy and there is significant risk to the mother from infection resulting from the breach in the integrity of the uterus. With the parents wailing and begging on one side for me to save their baby, and the Catholic institution where all this took place frowning on any activity that even hinted at assisting termination, I made a decision that resulted in many sleepless nights, regrets, and self-deprecation.

Without any published information for guidance, I gave the mother a round of antibiotics, continued the anti-labor medications, put her on strict bed rest with the bed tilted in a head-down position, had a catheter inserted to empty her bladder (with the bowel function to be dealt with when the need arose), and reviewed the numerous risks and potential complications with the parents. They both enthusiastically accepted the option and the risks, with the mother having no objection to lying in bed, head-down and immobile for up to three weeks or more. I also undertook a routine of doing a sterile examination of the cervix and dangling

---

[1] This was likely due to the reduction in the size of the uterus, which was suddenly holding half of its previous volume.

umbilical cord twice a day, during morning and evening rounds, seven days a week, for my partners had scornfully derided me for my plans to prolong the pregnancy, flatly stating that it was an unattainable goal. And I was well aware that should any serious complications arise for the mother, my decision and actions would be immediately put under scrutiny by my colleagues and detractors.

And thus, things progressed.

Julia continued to judiciously follow all that was required of her, and her remaining fetus in turn remained healthy and grew appropriately. Her cervix actually closed over the protruding umbilical cord, which continued to shrivel and blacken. My twice daily vaginal rinsing with antibiotic solution may or may not have been doing any good, as I had no published guidance, but no evidence of infection was noted within the uterus. And thus, she remained pregnant into the 22nd and then the 23rd week of the pregnancy. And unbelievably, the day came when she actually reached 24 weeks. I secretly hoped I could keep her at our institution to continue her personalized care, but I was also aware that I was running on borrowed time, and if the baby delivered before 32 weeks, the best care would be provided if that delivery occurred at a specialized facility.

And so, arrangements were made for the transfer.

With a prolonged hug and exuberant expressions of gratitude from Julia, I watched her transfer into the ambulance. She arrived at the receiving institution, where her care was managed by specialists who would have never attempted to keep her pregnant after the first baby's delivery, but were now obligated to continue her care. During my follow-up calls I cringed when I found out that she was no longer kept head-down, and in fact was given walking bathroom privileges, and allowed to sit in a chair for a few hours a day. The vaginal antibiotic washings were also discontinued as there were no documented, published benefits. And within a week after her transfer Julia presented evidence of infection, and the second baby was delivered via cesarean.

Premature delivery at 24-25 weeks of gestation is fraught with complications. There is at best a 75% chance of survival, but only a 25% chance of intact survival – that is, survival without severe, long-term complications such as cerebral palsy, blindness, or bowel damage. But these statistics apply to all deliveries at this gestational period. In cases where the baby is stressed, or undergoes prolonged attempts at stopping labor, the stress appears to accelerate the baby's maturation, so these newborns actually do much better than the statistics would suggest. And having been under stress for three weeks, I expected this baby to do the best of all.

But it was not to be.

Julia's baby survived, but spent an eternity in the intensive care unit. She developed every complication associated with prematurity, including eye damage, brain bleeding, severed cerebral palsy, and evidence of serious, permanent neurologic deficits. She finally was released to home with a feeding tube, the need for 24-hours a day care, and a very poor prognosis for significant improvement.

Shortly after dismissal the proud new parents came to my office with their bundle of joy. Julia demonstrated all of the characteristics of a new mother, proudly holding up her daughter with all of her dangling tubes, lines and monitor wires, and thanking me for all I had done to help her achieve her dream of motherhood. And the irony of it all weighed upon me like a leaden curtain. I knew that if any mother would be capable of providing the decades-long intensive care that this baby required, it would be Julia. I also wondered if she was even vaguely aware of the hellish road of complications and ordeals that lay before her.

Julia and her husband moved out of the area shortly afterwards. She continued to update me regularly with cards and pictures and reports on her baby's progress, and reading between the lines it was clear that her baby continued to have one medical complication, one middle-of-the-night emergency after another. At some point the husband decided it was all too much, and walked away from the marriage, the baby, the financial strain, and the devoted and hard-working mother. And around its second birthday the baby developed a complication that was too much for its damaged body and the overburdened medical system, and she finally expired, never achieving any of the milestones that mothers universally anticipate and excitedly share.

And I continued to wonder.

Did I do Julia and her husband any good, or did I unnecessarily complicate their lives, empty their bank accounts, and destroy their marriage.

Did I make a mistake by transferring her to the cold, impersonal and rigid institution, where rules were rigorously followed and innovation frowned upon.

Would they and their baby have been better off if I had continued the intense, daily, personalized care that I was providing, or would that have just complicated the situation even more.

I wanted to ask Julia if it was worth it, given the outcome, but then I realized the silliness of the question, for what mother would answer: 'No- I wish you had let my baby die as God intended'.

Maybe there is a reason that the books and the experts advise against prolonging the pregnancy under those circumstances, and the fault wasn't with the specialists, but with the one who thought he could make a difference.

For a very long time I carried the burden of this guilt[1].

---

[1] In all fairness, this course of action has been attempted since, much more successfully. The record for the longest time separating the delivery of twins is 90 days in 1996, and another case of twins 87 days apart, since then.

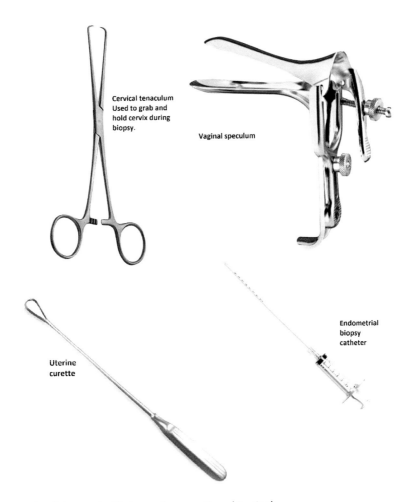

Cervical tenaculum
Used to grab and
hold cervix during
biopsy.

Vaginal speculum

**Endometrial
biopsy
catheter**

**Uterine
curette**

Basic tools of the trade (Note- not proportional in size).
Clockwise, from top left: **Cervical tenaculum**-two teeth lock together within
the cervix to help mobilize and steady during biopsy. It doesn't hurt as bad as
it looks; **Vaginal speculum**-inserted while closed, then opened and locked to
help visualization. Comes in a variety of sizes for different patients;
Endometrial biopsy catheter- the thin tube is inserted into uterus, suction
applied via syringe, and drawn back and forth to obtain tissue. Not visible, but
the end of the tube has an opening on the side and an adjacent sharp reverse
tooth; **Uterine curette**- inserted inside uterus and drawn back & forth to
evacuate contents.

Plate-1

Fetal length, crown of head to rump, per weeks of gestation.

1	0.03in	12	3.5in
2	0.05in	14	4.7in
3	0.09in	16	5.7in
4	0.15in	18	6.6in
5	0.31in	20	11in
6	0.58in	22	12in
7	0.9in	24	14in

26+ weeks: approximately 1-inch every two weeks until delivery

Fetal Growth

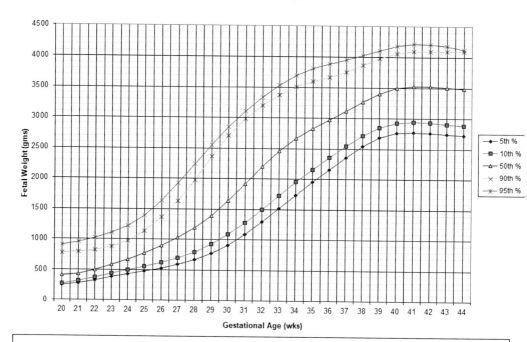

Fetal weight from 20 weeks of gestation to term. The 50th percent (black line with triangles) is the average. To convert grams to pounds divide by 454.

Plate-2

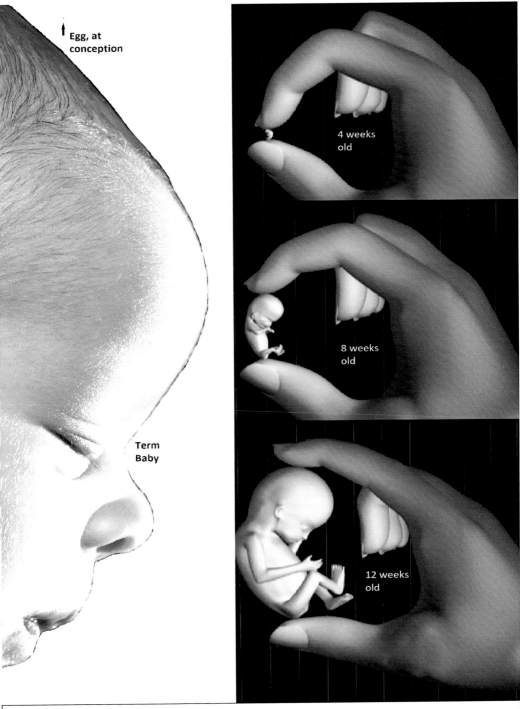

Egg, at conception

4 weeks old

8 weeks old

Term Baby

12 weeks old

Relative sizes during fetal development, in contrast to a newborn. The fertilized egg, shown at top left, above the arrow, is barely visible to the naked eye.

Plate-3

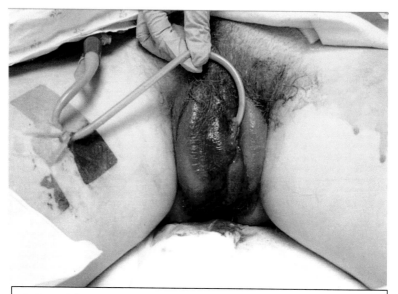

A. Post-delivery vulvar hematoma. A torn internal vessel resulted in the new mother losing significant blood under her genital skin. The tube being held is a catheter to empty her bladder.

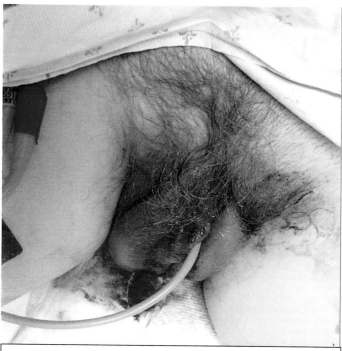

B. Post-delivery vulvar hematoma, same case as A.

Plate-4

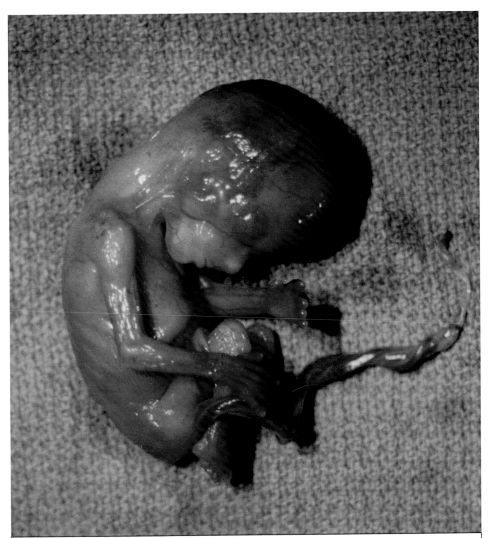

Spontaneous miscarriage which occurred during an office visit, for unknown reasons. Photo is close to actual size. Pregnancy was at 13 weeks, and fetus was about four inches, crown to rump length. Note perfectly formed hands and facial profile. The head is almost as long as the rest of the body. At this point, every organ is complete and in its adult location, with the exception of the testes in males.

Plate-5

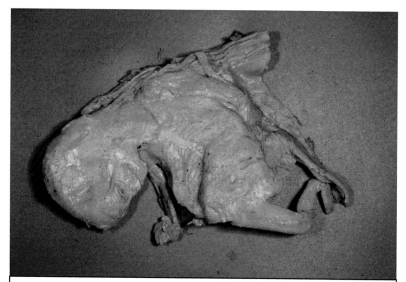

A. Incidental finding of a 'lost twin', at about 12-weeks of gestation. Companion twin delivered at term, healthy. Pregnancy was a presumed singleton until delivery and this discovery.

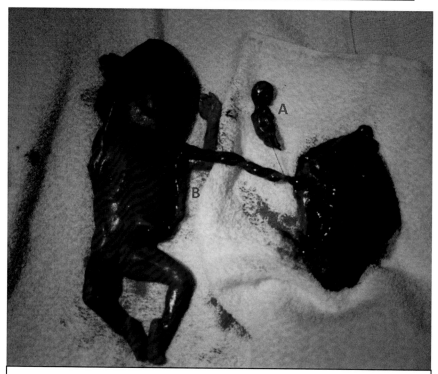

B. Mono-chorionic, mono-amniotic twins with cord entanglement. Twin A was at about 10-weeks of gestation, Twin B succumbed at 20-weeks.

Plate-6

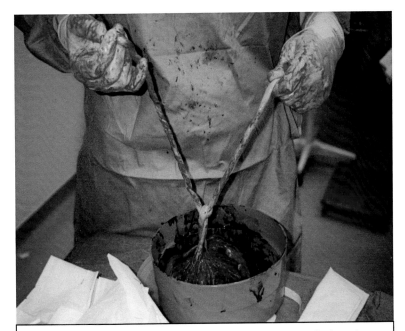

A. Common placenta from mono-chorionic, mono-amniotic twins, showing the entanglement of the umbilical cords. The picture was taken immediately after an emergent Cesarean delivery.

B. The twins from the above picture, at 17-years of age. They are obviously identical, yet distinctive.

Plate-7

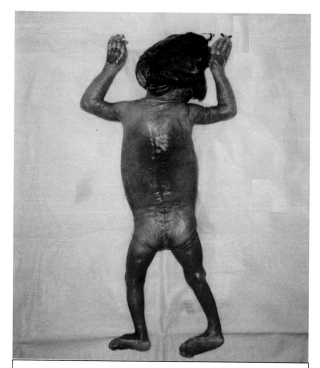

A. Result of egg fertilized with two sperm.

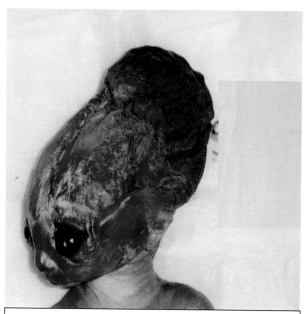

B. Same fetus as A; different view.

Plate-8

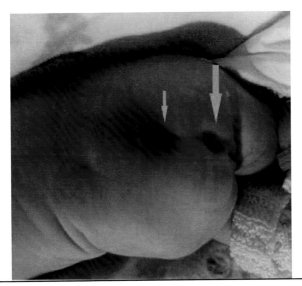

A. Spina Bifida, noted at birth. Large arrow points to the anal opening; smaller arrow to the defect. The cause is failure of the early nervous system to close at the posterior end. Not uncommon. Failure to close at the anterior end will result in failed brain development, and usually, but not always, loss of the pregnancy.

B. Ruptured twin ectopic pregnancy, in Fallopian tube, after removal.

Plate-9

A. Conjoined twins, Abby and Brittany. Now wonderful adults, they work as teachers, and their acceptance by their students speaks volumes about the innocence of youths.

B. Parasitic twin. Cause is thought to be very early split of the embryo, with subsequent reattachment. The abnormal location of reattachment leads to failure of development of one twin.

Plate-10

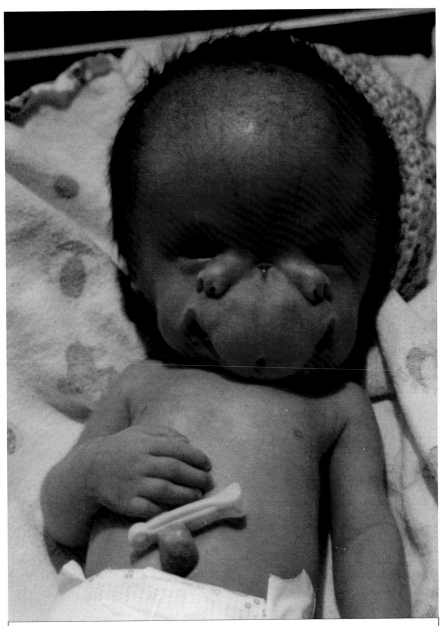

Diprosopus, or extreme late twinning. Perfectly normal male body, from neck down.

Plate-11

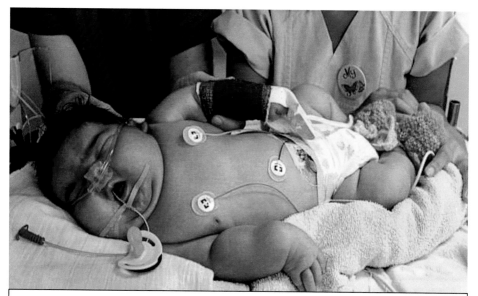

A. Rather robust baby, following vaginal delivery. One can only cringe thinking of what the mother had endured.

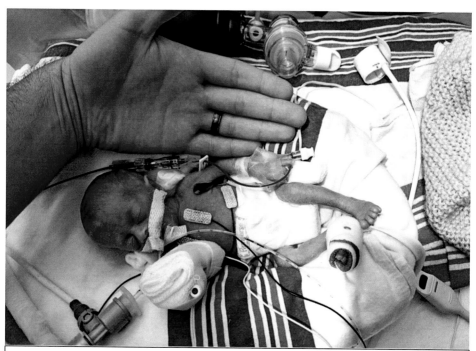

B. The other end of the spectrum: an extremely premature baby. Connor Florio, born at 23 weeks of gestation in 2018, weighing 310gms (just under 11oz). The diminutive fighter continues to do well.

Plate-12

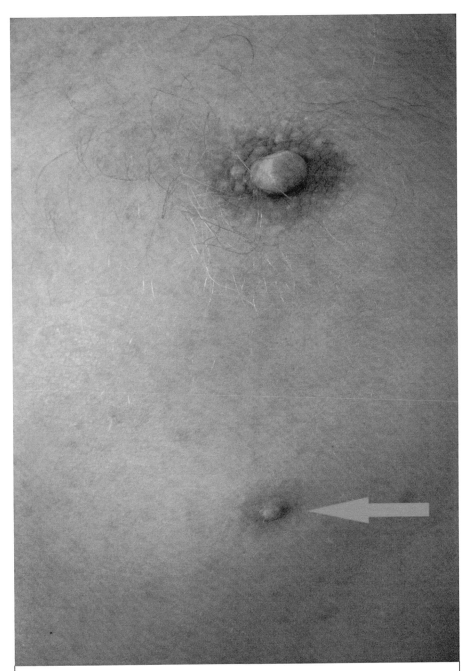

Polythelia – multiple nipples. Blue arrow points to second nipple. Not uncommon, and often mistaken for a mole, especially if flat.

Plate-13

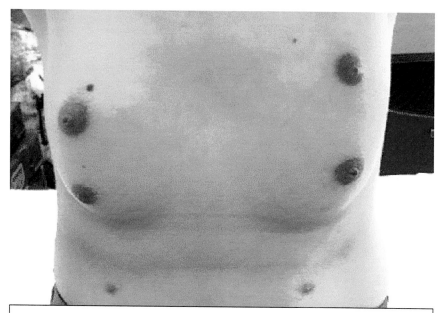

A. Polymastia – multiple breasts, with polythelia. Two breast pairs, with third nipple pair.

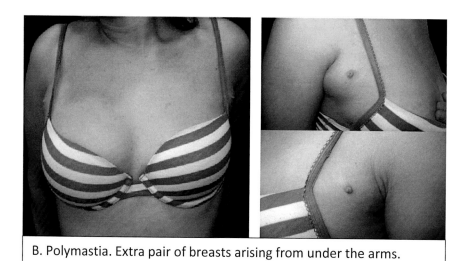

B. Polymastia. Extra pair of breasts arising from under the arms.

Plate-14

A. Male genital warts.

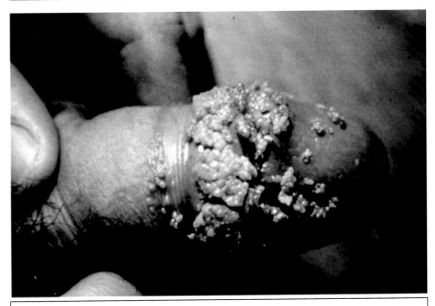

B. Male genital warts.

Plate-15

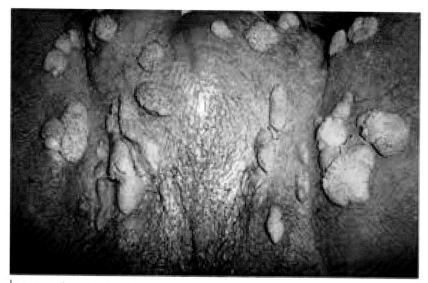

A. Female genital warts.

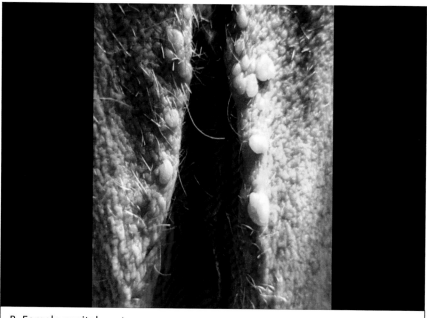

B. Female genital warts

Plate-16

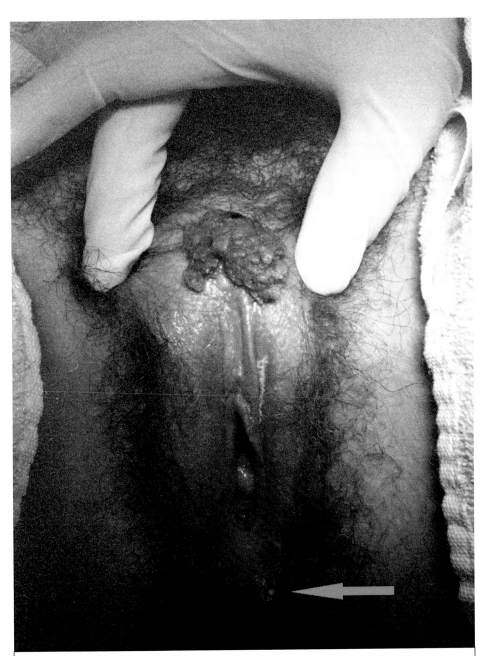

Female genital warts. Note large cluster between fingers. Blue arrow points to additional smaller cluster of lesions.

Plate-17

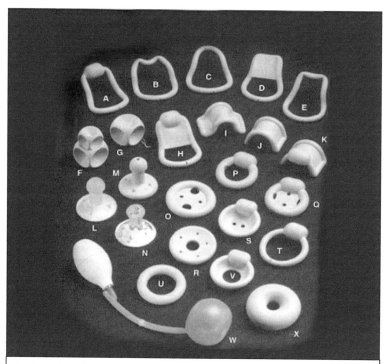

A. Sample collection of pessaries. Balloon pessary is labeled 'W'.

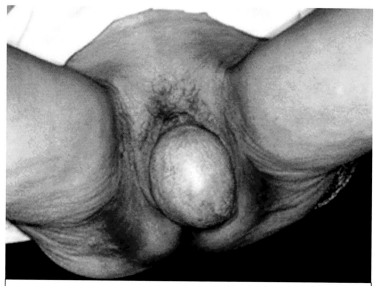

B. Vaginal prolapse in an elderly patient.

Plate-18

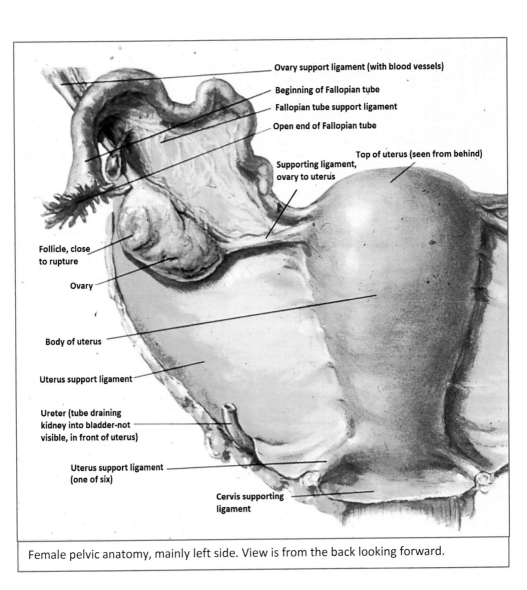

Ovary support ligament (with blood vessels)

Beginning of Fallopian tube

Fallopian tube support ligament

Open end of Fallopian tube

Top of uterus (seen from behind)

Supporting ligament, ovary to uterus

Follicle, close to rupture

Ovary

Body of uterus

Uterus support ligament

Ureter (tube draining kidney into bladder-not visible, in front of uterus)

Uterus support ligament (one of six)

Cervis supporting ligament

Female pelvic anatomy, mainly left side. View is from the back looking forward.

Plate-19

Happy outcomes. It's not all bad.

Plate-20

Of Trials & Tribulations

The ability of some patients to deny the existence of bad news sometimes bordered on the amazing.

I recall patients with progressive pain, who actually made and kept an office appointment to deal with the symptoms, who then refused further evaluation, such as an ultrasound or x-ray examination, out of fear that something bad or terminal would be discovered. And arguments about the fact that bad things can usually be treated, but only if diagnosed first, did not seem to carry any weigh. It is impossible to convey the frustration that one has to deal with, as a physician, in these circumstances.

The other side of the spectrum is equally amazing. Some patients appear to live their lives in anticipation of some malady, to explain some vague mental process that only they understand.

* * *

Beth was a professional lady, in her mid-40's, healthy and in a good relationship at home, with two children approaching the inevitable time to leave the nest[1]. She had been seen previously for unremarkable routine visits, until the day she called the office, frantic about a breast lump found on routine self-exam. Given the level of concern, I had her come in that day as the last patient. An office exam was unremarkable, with no distinct mass on my examination, even when directed by Beth to the area of concern. I did my best to reassure her, and she was scheduled for a mammogram forthwith. The mammogram was read as normal, but the patient insisted the lump was still there, so I ordered an ultrasound, which was also normal. Somewhat reassured, the matter was dropped – or so I believed.

---

[1] I always suspected this was at least partially responsible for her behavior.

144

About two months later, there was another call, regarding a lump in the other breast. The previous routine was repeated, starting with the visit at the end of the day (again, nothing on my examination), the mammogram, and the ultrasound. Once again, the patient was reassured, and the matter dropped.

And a few months later another frantic phone call from Beth, this time about a sensation of a mass in the lower abdomen, and concerns about ovarian tumors. Once again, the office visit and an ultrasound that revealed two normal ovaries and nothing untoward in the rest of the pelvis and abdomen. Knowing my ultrasound skills outside of the pelvis were not first rate, I also scheduled her for a CT-scan[1] of the abdomen and pelvis. And once again the results were negative and the patient reassured. But by now a pattern was beginning to emerge. I hinted to the office staff to expect a call from Beth about some other malady, and she did not disappoint, for a few weeks later she called about changes in her stool, and pain with bowel movements.

* * *

These cases are exceedingly difficult to manage. When the patient calls, there is immediate suspicion that there is nothing wrong, but the assumption is not absolute, for these patients do develop real issues, just like everyone else. As a result, every complaint demands full evaluation. If the concerns are stationary, that is, always involving the same area such as the breast, ovary, or menstrual issues, one can begin to plant the seed of

---

[1] CT-scan: Computed Tomography scan. A detailed 3-D x-ray examination of a body section, created by electronically putting together hundreds of individual 2-D x-ray pictures. Previously called 'CAT Scan', or 'Computed Axial Tomography' Scan.

the idea that perhaps there is need for a mental evaluation. Beth however, presented with roving symptoms, making the subject difficult to broach.

* * *

During training, physicians are taught that normal test results represent the middle range in a large population that has been tested. There are always perfectly normal patients who have some test result that will fall outside of the normal range, for no other reason that people are individuals, with individual variations. If one were to run ten random tests on a healthy patient, there is a good chance that one will be outside the range of normal. By the same token, if you do a head-to-toe CT scan on a healthy individual, there is an even chance that something abnormal will appear on one of the sections. Once an abnormality is identified, there is an obligatory need for investigation and identification, which often necessitates a surgical procedure. And any surgical procedure, even minor ones, carry the risk of complications. Some of these complications can be minor, such as bleeding in excess of normal, or severe, such as an entrenched infection, or even fatal[1].

Rare, but not unheard of, even with modern medicine and good care, but patients do die from even minor surgical procedures, and not because of

---

[1] During training I participated in a routine cesarean delivery, which was complicated afterwards by wound infection. Although treated appropriately as soon as it was identified, the infection became entrenched, spread, and the patient developed a condition called 'necrotizing fasciitis'. The only treatment available at this point is surgical removal of the infected tissues, which in her case involved a large portion of her abdominal wall, with extensive plastic surgery repairs and prolonged hospitalization. She eventually recovered and was dismissed to home, but her scarring was extensive and permanent, and her baby was close to walking before she healed enough to lift him up.

medical errors[1]. As a result, a scan that was not necessary nor indicated, exposes the patient to unnecessary procedures, expenses, and risks. This is the main reason it is emphasized during training that physicians should not do unnecessary or unindicated tests or evaluations, as there is the possibility that they will do more harm than good.

* * *

The final call from Beth resulted in a referral to a gastroenterologist[2]. His extensive evaluation revealed the presence of a growth in Beth's stomach, which resulted in a surgical procedure for excision. The mass turned out to be a rare and benign tumor, which could have stayed in place until Beth grew old and died of natural causes. Fortunately, she did well, and had an uncomplicated recovery. But I will never forget the comment from the specialist about how excited the patient was to find something was actually wrong with her. This final episode seemed to cure whatever ailed her, physically or mentally. Or perhaps it just addressed whatever secondary gain she needed, for there were no more frantic phone calls from her, and she became just another routine patient[3].

---

[1] Medical or medication errors are one more layer of risk in any procedure. Unfortunate, avoidable, but present nonetheless.

[2] Gastroenterologist: a specialist in digestive and bowel issues.

[3] For another example of extreme behavior, involving a litany of complaints, see page-204.

Denial

I ended up raising two boys, aged 18 months apart. As a result, I suddenly found myself with two teenagers, and double the usual trials and tribulations. We were also living in a small mid-western town, notorious at the time for the quantity of methamphetamine that was passed thru and distributed within its boundaries. And managing a busy practice, I was not always available to deal with my boys' peer issues. Knowing the risks, I found myself looking for an easy way to determine if the boys were being tempted.

Thru my contacts, I discovered a manufacturer that was offering custom drug screening kits to physicians. These were simple urine tests with multiple lines representing different compounds, and they could be customized and ordered with up to seven drug tests per kit. And best of all, in quantities of 50, the price was around $20 each. I immediately saw a solution to my concerns, and an opportunity to provide a useful service to my patients as well. I proceeded to order 50 kits, and specified screens for drugs that were popular in the community at the time.

* * *

Denial is a powerful emotion. It allows one to deal with stressful situations, or issues beyond one's control. It would not normally be considered a positive response, because obviously it can hinder the ability to deal with a problem, or the ability to seek an answer. However, it can present an easy option for a short-term solution.

I vividly recall a shy, petite young lady, 15-years-old, who was brought into the office by her mother, with a complaint of irregular menses – specifically, no flow for the past three months. In any woman of reproductive age, any gynecologic condition has to be approached with the assumption that the patient is pregnant until proven otherwise, and a pregnancy test is routinely carried out. And in this case, the test came back positive. Surmising that the mother was probably not aware of her daughter's covert adventures, I tried to speak with the young lady alone. The mother would have none of it.

Careful in my choice of words, I mentioned the test result, and the logical explanation for the absence of periods that was the source of angst. The young lady immediately turned bright red and dropped her gaze, for she obviously suspected the cause, even if she were unwilling to admit it.

On the other hand, the mother's reaction was something to behold. She immediately huffed and stated in no uncertain terms that my conclusion was ridiculous and that I must be mistaken, for her daughter was only 15, could not possibly be sexually active, and my tests and interpretations were obviously incompetent and in error.

During the mother's diatribe, I noticed that the young lady continued to look down and remain quiet. And the mother continued in her denial, without once consulting her daughter.

Without another comment or gesture from me, her anger continued to feed upon itself and grow, and finally, with a number of additional verbal opinions about my abilities, she grabbed her daughter's hand and stomped out.

I never saw either one again. But I did wonder how long the denial mechanism was employed, and the reaction to the inevitable conclusion when the daughter's belly continued to grow beyond what could be blamed on gas or excess food consumption, or ultimately, when the baby finally poked its head out to look around.

* * *

I recognized the same process when I began to offer the drug screening kits, at my cost, to patients that I knew had teenagers at home.

I kept eight of the kits for my own use, and a year later, at the end of the expiration date, I had 42 kits remaining. Not one patient took me up on the offer, for it was obvious that none of them had teenagers that would ever consider using illicit drugs. So why bother spending $20 to even look.

Pam and Her Periods - or how can anything bleed so much, for so long, and stay alive

My initial impression on meeting Pam was her obesity: A rotund five-foot tall woman with a shy demeanor, her weight I would soon find out topped my scale at over 300lbs. She was quietly and patiently waiting in an examining room for the arrival of the physician. Her chart listed her as a new patient, 48-years old, coming in for a problem directed visit. After a decade of private gynecology practice, I have learned not to react to the outward appearance of a patient and avoid the normal human snap judgments, instead working hard to keep an open mind and allowing the history and physical examination to guide the direction of the diagnosis. In Pam's case however, obtaining her history turned out to be a struggle in itself, taking up the better part of her visit. Her history turned out to be anything but routine. She was single, never having been pregnant, with a single episode of sexual activity in high school, details of which she was unwilling to share. And she was not gay.

* * *

She had been obese since childhood, and this had been the focal point of derision and ridicule by her peers going back to when she was a kindergartener, and accentuated later in life by insensitive adults. In her adult life, she was acutely aware of the stares and snickers of strangers - some of it real, but I suspected much of it was imaginary, the result of self-consciousness and learned behavior. While listening to her story, a contrast became apparent in her features. If one were willing to look beyond the obesity and her body's storage of fat in unusual places, such as the ear lobes, Pam was actually a very attractive lady. She was blessed with bright hazel eyes, lovely hair, full lips, and when she was prodded, goaded,

153

teased, and finally pushed a bit, a smile that lit up her face. Even her shy demeanor contributed to her attractiveness. After the initial visit, as she became comfortable around me, finally accepting that I would not be mean or dismissive, and she was willing to let down her guard somewhat, it also became obvious that Pam had a sharp wit and bright intelligence that was deeply hidden behind her self-defense mechanisms. She also had one of the most artistically attractive, perfectly aligned and flowing writing scripts I have ever seen. Unfortunately, her psyche had been scarred for so many decades, by so many people and in so many, many mean ways, that Pam's attractiveness was mired in a deep pit of self-consciousness, surrounded by impenetrable walls, and appeased by an endless line of snacks, poor food choices, and apathy about life in general.

Pam's visit to me was initiated by a family member, concerned over Pam's persistent complaints of frequent, irregular and very heavy menstrual bleeding, followed by a deep fatigue that would take days, sometimes weeks to resolve. She had been seen on a number of occasions by her small-town family physician, who had diagnosed recurrent, significant anemia, and had treated her casually with the usual recommendation of increased red meat intake, multi-vitamins and frequent doses of iron supplements – a combination that would constipate the Mississippi river. And it appeared that no one had ever tried to workup or manage or understand the underlying cause.

The menstrual cycle is a complex ballet on a stage populated by hormone dancers and choreographed by the team of hypothalamus and pituitary, two primitive structures deeply imbedded within the brain. While the individual steps have been teased out over many years of research, the fine nuances and roles of many of the backstage players remain mysterious. The background is defined by the need to provide a nourishing bed for the potential fetus. This necessitates a thick, deeply engorged lining in the uterus, able to provide a healthy flow of nourishing blood for the embryo, and able to increase dramatically in volume as the fetus develops. As of necessity, it is thick and able to grow with need. This lining is in turn very fragile & unstable and, if allowed to persist, is one of the few tissues in the body that will, in its natural course, become first abnormal in appearance, with a good probability of eventually becoming cancerous. The body has thereby developed a clever system to deal with the needs of reproduction. The lining is slowly built up during the first half of each menstrual cycle, reaching the peak of lush growth around the time that a fertilized egg would be expected to arrive. And if the egg is not there at the expected time, the lining is self-limiting, and as a result of changes in the background hormones it is shed over a few days, returning the uterus to its base, benign state, at which point the process repeats for the next cycle. This results in the monthly bleeding cycle that is the bane of the adult female, and an endless source of humor for the rest.

There are numerous places along the path where the process can go astray. For example, the process depends on a precise balance of hormones, hormone management signals, and feedback mechanisms to maintain checks and balances. The complexity of the process means that it doesn't take much to throw it out of alignment. One of the most common causes in developed societies is obesity.

One of the signals that the body uses to maintain control over the process is our friend Estrogen[1]. This hormone, uniquely functional in the

---

[1] While Estrogen is a unique mammalian hormone, many other substances are similar enough to interact or interfere with its receptor. These include - but are not limited to - plant substances, byproducts of fungi, and manmade substances such as BPA. Significant exposure to any of these will trigger the same response, and can interfere with the normal functions of the body's hormone and cycle.

mammalian female, is produced by the ovaries, and its level is a measure of the activity of the ovary during the cycle, much as the temperature of a room is a measure of the functioning of the heater, controlled via feedback by the thermostat.

As it so happens, Estrogen is present in three forms. The most common, the one that the body uses to evaluate the functioning of the ovary, and the one with the most potent signal and feedback, is Estradiol. There is another form, called Estriol, which we can ignore at this time, since its only function is during pregnancy. The third form is Estrone. This hormone happens to be produced naturally and steadily, in small quantities, by fat storage cells. The underlying function is unknown, although it may be a casual byproduct of the cells, or it may serve as a precursor for another signal.

Normally, the limited level of production and the low level of reactivity with the primary hormone equate to Estrone having no bearing on the menstrual cycle. The problem arises when there is an abundance of fat storage cells. As these cells increase in size & number, the production of Estrone climbs, until a threshold is reached and the body's balanced mechanism is disrupted. One of the consequences is that the normal cycle of egg release is interrupted (in the adult female, fertility is decreased in proportion to the increase in BMI beyond a normal range). Another consequence is that the normal house cleaning at the end of the month is no longer thorough, and the presence of the intruding hormone stimulates continuing, unopposed growth of the lining, with consequences ranging from irregular bleeding, to heavy and prolonged bleeding and, if allowed to continue, eventual cancerous changes. This is why prolonged, heavy, and most importantly, irregular bleeding needs to be addressed as a medical problem, not just an inconvenience.

During the review of her history Pam couldn't recall if she ever had regular periods. Her menstrual cycles started around the same time as her peers, but while they talked about monthly bleeding consisting of a few days of tampons or pads, Pam dealt with days and days, and sometimes weeks, of bleeding, tampons by the truckload, and frequent calls by her parents to the plumber to deal with the clogged sewer system. It would be a fair bet that some of her uterine lining hadn't been cleared out for decades. And of course, none of this was addressed by the attempts of her previous physician to deal with the issue by treating the consequences – anemia – rather than the problem.

The first step in treating a 48-year-old woman with a history of years of irregular periods is to ensure that nothing bad has already happened. This involves obtaining a sample of the lining for the pathologist to review. It's really a simple procedure, involving passing a small tube (about the diameter of a cell phone ear jack and about a foot and a half long) into the uterus. The tube has a medium syringe on the outside to provide suction, and a reverse hook on the inserted end to scrape off the sample. It's a quick and simple office procedure, needing no anesthetic since the only untoward experience is some brief cramping. The normal expectation is a scant amount of tissue or blood at the very end of the syringe upon completion. Invariably, the explanation of the procedure results in the full spectrum of expressions, from shock to raw terror, loss of color, and invariable tremors on the part of the patient. Pam was no exception, and the fact that she had never born children made the procedure somewhat more difficult and uncomfortable. The surprising part was the quantity of tissue that literally filled the syringe. Not a good sign. And what was even more worrisome was the unexpected call from the pathologist within 48 hours (usual turnaround is three to seven days, and even then, the results are forwarded electronically). In this case the pathologist reported the presence of wide-spread cancer, with primitive appearing cells suggestive of a nasty malignancy.

Women have a list of cancers unique to their reproductive anatomy. In descending order of frequency in western cultures these are sited at the uterus, cervix and ovary (although some would argue that breast cancer, by far the most frequent of all, belongs at the head of the list, I will disagree only because breast cancer also strikes men, although at about one tenth the frequency seen in females). In terms of lethality, the order is reversed, with ovarian cancer first (most of which are well advanced at diagnosis), followed by cervical and finally uterine cancer. One of the main reasons that uterine cancer is at the bottom of the lethality list is due to the fact that diagnosis is often made early in the disease, which is preceded by prolonged, heavy and irregular bleeding. Unless of course, the bleeding has been going on for years, and ignored.

* * *

One of the more dreaded of all office visits are the ones setup to review bad results. This was no exception, and Pam suspected something was up when I requested the presence of a trusted family member. This is done so the patient has a support person as well as another set of ears present when the bad news and associated information are presented, for patients will frequently stop listening after the word 'cancer' is uttered.

Pam took the news rather better than expected, which should not have been a surprise, considering what life had thrown at this woman for nearly half a century. I explained that treatment involved extensive surgery with removal of all of her reproductive organs, possible radiation, and that the stage would be determined at that point.

Staging, along with grade are the best predictors of survival with any given cancer. Pam already had been diagnosed with grade-3, the worst. It only remained to be seen how far the cancer had spread. It is notable at this point that the pathologist, while reviewing his findings, had mentioned that Pam's uterine cancer was the most malignant example he had ever seen, with numerous abnormal cells in the process of dividing, and many bizarre forms present. On the other hand, he felt that the cancer, with its high level of activity, should respond very well to chemotherapy.

* * *

I had already scheduled an appointment with a gynecologist who specialized in cancer treatment (Pam's care at this point was well beyond my level of training), and the surgery was performed shortly afterwards. The cancer appeared to be limited to the pelvis (stage-3 out of four) and chemotherapy was scheduled for four weeks later, to allow healing to complete. Post operatively Pam did surprisingly well, considering the fact that obesity markedly increases the risk of surgical complications. I did not have any follow-up visits scheduled, nor did I expect to hear from her, since her care at this point was out of my hands. I was therefore surprised to find out that she had scheduled an urgent visit with me one week before her recovery was considered complete.

It came out that she had suffered a seizure at home.

Once again, she was in the office, waiting with a resigned attitude. She had no recollection of events preceding the seizure, although she had been suffering silently with worsening headaches over the past two weeks. A family member present at the time described classic grand mal seizure symptoms, lasting just a few minutes. This was something totally new in Pam's life. I immediately ordered a scan of her head, and within hours the cause was identified: Pam had three distinct masses in her brain, consistent with metastatic disease. This news was shocking for a number of reasons, but primarily that the suspected source, the uterine cancer, is not known to spread to the brain. Its propensity is local spread, and in advanced cases the cancerous cells may lodge as far as the lungs. It is a testament to the aggressiveness of the disease that at what should have been stage three, they had actually found their way deep into the brain matter, and by their presence and growth triggered a seizure, and upped the staging to stage four, the worst possible. At this point, on top of everything else that was going on, Pam's care took a tragic turn.

The first step in any new onset seizure is to prevent a recurrence, since seizures, if sustained, can be deadly. Our small community had recently recruited a Neurologist (specialist in diseases of the nervous system), and a Neurosurgeon. The two were in practice together, and eager to build their patient population. Naturally I referred Pam to the Neurologist, who agreed to see her that day. Couple of days later I received an update, and was surprised to see that the Neurologist had referred Pam to the co-tenant Neurosurgeon, who had recommended surgical excision.

It must be pointed out that surgical excision of most tumor metastases[1] are done for palliative reasons, that is, to provide relief and an improvement in the quality of a limited life, because in most cases there are many more sites of cancer spread than those that can be identified or surgically removed. While Pam's brain metastases were a significant quality of life issue, the seizures could have been controlled with medication, and chemotherapy allowed a chance to reverse the course of the disease. Surgery and its attendant need for recovery would of necessity

---

[1] Metastasis: spread of a cancer to an area away from the site of origin. Pleural form is 'metastases'.

delay chemotherapy for another few weeks, and we had already seen an example of the aggressiveness of this tumor.

But at this point it was neither my time nor place to guide her care. And neither Pam nor her one family member asked my opinion. The surgery was scheduled, pre-surgical scans revealed no other sites of spread, and the tumors were successfully excised. Within two weeks Pam suffered another seizure, was admitted to the hospital, and a scan revealed numerous new growths in her brain, as well as her chest. Her course at this point was rapidly downhill, and she went into multiple organ failure, never having had a chance to go home.

I avoid social visits to terminal patients primarily because I find them emotionally draining, and also because as medical students we are taught from the beginning of our training that the best medical care is provided by someone who is not emotionally attached.

But I feared that Pam might be alone during her final days, and so I made an excuse to stop by. As I had suspected she was alone, sedated, with bandages around her head. She was reposed in a decoratively sterile hospital room with a bedside stand holding a half empty container of tasteless institutional apple sauce. Next to it was a single vase, half filled with discolored water, holding a few wilted and unidentifiable plants draped over the lip. Alongside, hanging forlornly over the edge of the stand, was a partially deflated balloon with the ironic expression 'Get Well Soon' legible on its side.

Three or four cards were scattered about on the stand.

She awakened at my arrival, her face lit up, and she managed a smile through what must have been a thick fog of pain and medication.

The visit was strained and uncomfortable, and I found myself wanting to make an excuse to leave, and yet prolonging the visit knowing this would be the last time I would see her. I commended her on her attitude considering all that she had been thru, which she attributed to having lived her life with the expectation that each negotiated peak would throw another obstacle, burden, or tragedy her way.

Thankfully I received a page at this point, and as I finally prepared to make my leave she reached to the table and handed me one of the cards laying there. The card turned out to be sealed and had my name on it.

I suddenly realized that all of the cards were from her, not to her.

She explained that her intent was to have it delivered after her death, but since I was there, I might as well have it. With sincere thanks and an awkward squeeze of her hand, I bid a final farewell.

At the nurse's station, half distracted while responding to my page, I opened the card. There, in that beautifully even, artistic script, surprisingly intact even with all that her mind had endured, was a thank you note. Thanking me for all I had done for her, and lamenting the fact that a caring physician hadn't taken care of her earlier in her life, for then she wouldn't have had such a negative attitude, and perhaps would have sought medical care sooner. She thanked me for not always focusing on her obesity, and for treating her with dignity and respect. I quickly left, making sure to look away so the nurses on duty wouldn't see the welling tears.

* * *

I have kept that card to this day, and look at it once in a while, and still marvel at the beautiful script, the geometrically even lines, and the suffering soul of the writer in between the words. I wonder at all that could have been and was never experienced or tragically and prematurely taken away. I wonder how things would have turned out if I hadn't referred Pam to local physicians trying to build a practice and demonstrate need and income.

I wonder if the brain surgery was really necessary, and I wonder at the repeated, unfortunate roll of the dice that condemned this talented, intelligent and innately beautiful person to a life on the fringe, culminating in a tragically painful, premature, and ultimately lonely end.

If there is a Heaven, I can only hope that Pam has a place near the head of the table, for her humility and quiet, life-long suffering on Earth has surely earned her that spot.

Sandy, who wasn't really Sandy

I had the good fortune of working with an infertility specialist during my training as a resident. Beyond the usual background knowledge of the female fertility cycle, I came to an understanding of some the problems that occasionally prevent the system from progressing along the expected paths, and how as physicians we can address the issues, netting us a grateful patient as well as a new obstetrical case. The latter has to be one of the most rewarding aspects of the career. An unusually happy, healthy patient, one who intently hangs onto every word of advice, dutifully follows instructions, religiously keeps appointments, and the process culminates in one of the happiest moments in anyone's experience. The downside of course is the depth of the patients' sorrow and anger when things don't proceed as expected.

As it turned out, none of this applied to Sandy.

She presented on her initial visit as a very attractive 20-year-old, with short cropped hair, and a demeanor that belied her 5-foot, 2-inch frame. She was proportionate, with an athletic build, and a rigid yet comfortable posture, even when seated, and a politeness when answering questions that comes from a military background and training. This was confirmed by her chart, which also revealed that she was married, and accompanied by her husband. He was seated next to her, with similar posture and demeanor, equally attractive in his masculine way. The pair could have posed for a U.S. Olympic Team recruitment poster. They had made the appointment for an infertility consult, and I immediately jumped ahead (too prematurely, it turned out) and pictured the attractive couple in the birthing center, following my successful intervention, laboring under my supervision, and the envy of my colleagues.

Sandy had had a normal childhood and maintained growth and development along with her peers, until that age when girls start to change from children to women. This typically begins (in Western culture, and there are differences in different cultures) around age eight or nine, initiated by the growth of tissue under the nipples, heralding the future breast, and the source of much self-consciousness. This is shortly accompanied by an increase in the rate of growth, increased pigmentation, density and coarseness of body hair, especially in the genital and underarm regions, and the increase in the production and composition of perspiration by specialized sweat glands in the same areas. This in turn leads to changes in the bacteria that normally colonize the skin, with consequent alteration in the production of aromatic components (think 'pheromones', via bacterial gas production), and the foundation for the billions of dollars spent annually on antiperspirants, deodorants, perfumes, and myriad other products and services designed to mask or alter the natural, normal, and ultimately, inevitable.

* * *

The internal changes in the female are equally profound. The ovaries, which have been quiescent until now, begin to enlarge, and develop multiple small cysts. Each of these innumerable cysts is destined to either mature and ultimately release an egg (in a desperate attempt at perpetuation of the species) or whither & die, in an inevitable cycle mimicking life itself. The process is orchestrated and maintained by a complex choreography of hormonal signals, feedbacks, and checks and balances. As to the mechanism that begins the process, no one is really sure of the origin of the initial triggering event or signal. We do know that it begins with maturation of certain specialized cells deep in the brain, in a region called the hypothalamus. This area signals other specialized hormone secreting cells in the pituitary gland (also deep within the brain), which in turn produce a pair of signals that engage with the ovaries in an intricate dance designed to select the most robust egg and nurture it to maturity, release, and hopefully, fertilization. During the selection process (which occurs in most women during their reproductive years at four-week intervals) dozens of cysts are recruited each month, but usually only one matures & releases the egg[1]. The remaining cysts - the has been and never were - will simply die off and leave a tiny bit of scar tissue as a reminder. The last ones are used up around the age of 50 (again, in western cultures), and at this time, with all of the primordial eggs gone, and a precipitous drop in the Estrogen that they produce, the woman experiences menopause, another phase of life.

* * *

The framework for all this is laid down during the development of the female fetus, during the first trimester of life in the three months following fertilization and implantation. The absence of a Y-chromosome leads to the development of female internal organs from the growing tissues. This is an important distinction, and the source of some unusual conditions, for to develop as a male, there has to be intervention from the Y-chromosome. In its absence, or in the case of defects of the signal, or the messenger, or the receptor within the tissues, the default will be a female. It's common knowledge that males have a Y-chromosome as well as an X-chromosome (former from the father, latter from the mom), while females have two of the X-chromosome only, one from each parent. What isn't commonly known is the fact that without the Y, the

---

[1] Of course, in some women occasionally two, or rarely, three or more, eggs are released, and the result is the human equivalent of the double-yolk egg. If both get fertilized, well, aren't those future moms in for a surprise.

development will be female: X-null will be a girl, as well as an XX, an XXX, and so on.

Damage one particular small area on the Y-chromosome, the male signal zone, and you will end up with a perfectly normal girl with X-Y. Damage the gene producing the signal, the signal itself, or the receptor for the signal and you'll end up with a girl. Damage the gene for producing Testosterone, or its receptor, and you'll end up with a girl, for the female is the default sex (this will undoubtedly lead to some interesting late night social and cultural arguments as well as fodder for comic relief).

* * *

The system remains quiet during childhood, although continuing to mature and develop more secure communication links among the various players. And then at some predetermined point in the child's continuing maturation, the system begins to apply its influence. In females in western culture, the onset is typically around the age of eight, and initially manifested by increasing fullness in the breasts. The underlying signal is Estrogen, which has been steadily increasing in concentration in the blood, originating from primitive follicles within the ovaries – the precursors of the future eggs. A young girl's body is exquisitely sensitive to Estrogen, and even minor increases will result in a response from the receptive tissues. These include the aforementioned breasts, which begin depositing fat and increasing the milk producing glands, the associated ducts, and the thickening and increased pigmentation of the overlying skin & nipple. Other responsive tissues are sweat glands within the underarms and genital area, the hair follicles in the same regions, and certain fat cells, which start to store in a peculiar distribution, ultimately changing the indistinct asexual shape of the female child into the curves of a young woman. Incidentally, this particular distribution of fat is universally perceived by males as attractive, as it identifies a female as being able to conceive and produce enough Estrogen to make attempts at conception worthwhile.

Interestingly, although reproduction has long ceased to be the primary motivation for human sexual activity, the primitive signal basis for this attraction is still intact. Hence, the universal attractiveness of the hourglass female figure.

So, what happens when things don't go right?

Going back to the fetus, it's important to understand the mechanism for developing into a male. There are actually two separate signals with their respective receptors. The first, as previously mentioned, is part of the Y-chromosome. The primary function of this signal is to suppress the development of the female internal parts (the precursors of the fallopian tubes, uterus, cervix and vagina), and promotion of the male internal parts (the prostate, the testes and their descent mechanism, and the sperm conduction system). The specialized tissues that will become the future gonads[1] begin the same in both sexes. The default development will be ovaries, but in the presence of the normally functioning Y-chromosome, it will develop into the testes, and shortly begin Testosterone production, the second signal, which will in turn induce the external male sex appearance. The testes continue their normal Testosterone production more or less steadily, until puberty, at which point the level markedly rises[2].

---

[1] Gonads: a non-gender specific term for reproductive organs, such as the testes in the male, and the ovaries in the female.
[2] In the female, the ovaries remain quiescent until puberty. The female appearance of the baby is promoted by the mother's Estrogen.

There are a number of unusual situations that can arise, and all have been reported at one time or another. In rare cases, for poorly understood reasons (but probably triggered by partially defective receptors) some fetuses develop both sex gonads, with an ovary on one side and a testicle on the other, or a mix of the two in the same gonad. The final appearance at birth is dependent on the level of the conflicting hormones, and is frequently indeterminate. These individuals are labeled 'hermaphrodites'.

Another example of confusion in sex determination is seen in babies that have a defect in their body's steroid pathways. If they are X-Y, these newborns appear genetically appropriate, but suffer from a number of medical issues, which are serious but reasonably managed once identified. If however, they are X-X females, the abnormality causes an elevation of intermediate hormones that resemble Testosterone. As these hormone levels rise, they begin to exert influence on the external genital development of the fetus. Since the Y-Chromosome suppression is absent, internally these infants are female, but their external appearance is, depending on the levels involved, indeterminate or male. If the assignment of the newborn's sex is done with enthusiasm, one is left announcing 'it's a boy!', only to have to shortly revise the announcement to 'it's a girl!'. Fortunately, the misidentification is usually quickly discovered when the underlying medical conditions is diagnosed. But there have been mild cases that have resulted in the wrong sex assignment for years before corrective action was taken.

* * *

In one of the more unfortunate examples, the receptor for the initial signal establishing maleness is defective, but the defect is not complete. As previously noted, the default sex takes over, and the child is born and develops during childhood as a normal female, although the genetic composition is an X-Y male. Things go along fine for the unsuspecting child and parents, and the girl grows and develops appropriately until puberty kicks in.

At this point, it needs to be pointed out that every regulating system in the body has in turn a negative feedback system in place (without which the organism would not survive for very long) [1]. Eat a meal, and stomach acid kicks in. But as soon as the acid production picks up, a negative feedback system begins to crank it down again, to prevent excess production from dissolving the stomach itself.

But in these aforementioned children, the feedback, which depends on the same receptor for Testosterone, the male hormone of puberty, is also defective. As a result of the absence of the negative feedback, at puberty the Testosterone level rises, and keeps on rising well beyond the normal levels. It reaches many times the level that the system expects, at which point the less than 100% defect in the receptor comes into play.

One needs to understand at this point that in the area of external anatomy, females and males are quite similar, and for the most part, correspondingly located [2]. The penis equivalent in the female is the

---

[1] There are only two exceptions, and interestingly, both are present in the female. See page 195.

[2] In the adult some of the structures regress to the point where one needs a microscope to make it out, they are there nonetheless. There is however one very significant difference in the layout: The abdominal cavity in males is sealed against the outside world, whereas in women there remains an open pathway, via the internal opening of the fallopian tube, the uterus, the cervix, and the vagina. Sexually transmitted infections in the male, while potentially devastating to the reproductive potential, tend to remain within the genital tract. In women,

clitoris, and the scrotum is represented by the midline fusion of the labia. And while by external appearance it's difficult to completely transition from a male to a female without surgery, the move in the other direction is quite feasible, and can occur in the presence of hormones alone[1].

And therein lies the final tragic turn in these children. Having developed and been raised as perfectly normal girls, at puberty, with the markedly elevated level of Testosterone, the receptors are finally awakened from their slumber.

And suddenly in the midst of puberty, which is already an emotionally trying time in any adolescent's life, the girl begins changing, not into a woman, but into a man.

* * *

The term Hermaphrodite (Intersex is also used to prevent stigmatizing the individual) is often bandied about while discussing abnormal sexual development, but true hermaphrodism is quite rare. By medical definition, these individuals will have both ovarian and testicular tissues – which again, is exceedingly rare. More commonly the term is applied, inappropriately, to individuals having ambiguous genitals, properly termed pseudo-hermaphrodites.

* * *

---

infections can spread into the abdominal cavity leading to permanent scarring, infertility, and even death if not identified and properly treated.

[1] Give a female child or adult male hormones, and her clitoris will enlarge into a semblance of a penis, and her labia will fuse in the midline, resembling a scrotum. She will grow facial hair in a male pattern, her voice will deepen, and if older, she will develop male pattern baldness. If she has already developed breasts they will lose some of their structure, but will not regress completely.

Pseudo-hermaphrodism, also rare but much more common than the true variety, is a condition where the genetic or gonadal makeup (either ovary or testicle) doesn't match the appearance of the individual.

In the case of a genetic female with male appearance, the condition is usually caused by steroid production defects that lead to increased production of masculinizing hormones, or less likely, by abnormal production in the mother during the pregnancy[1].

In the case of genetic males, the condition leading to feminization would have to involve a defect in the male hormone or its receptor, or a sudden high Estrogen production from the mother that crosses the placenta and overwhelms the receptors of the fetus[2].

* * *

Another rare but unfortunate miscue is seen in a condition called precocious, or premature puberty. Any onset of the signs of puberty in a female prior to age six is considered premature, and a sign of some malfunction in the system resulting in the inappropriate production of Estrogen. Precocious puberty can, in rare cases, be triggered by tumors that produce Estrogen without any guiding signal, but most often they have no underlying cause. Suddenly the young girl begins showing signs of transformation into a woman, but the only thing maturing (prematurely) is the body. The mind, the psyche, the behavior, the pleasures, needs and desires all belong to that of a young child.

---

[1] Most of these conditions in the mother would cause immediate infertility. The only exceptions would be conditions that develop after the woman becomes pregnant.
[2] Usually from an ovarian estrogen producing tumor in the mother.

I had occasion to witness this phenomenon while in residency. The patient was an 8-year-old child from the inner city where my training program was based.

I came across LaDonna during an unrelated visit to the pediatric clinic. She was sitting in a corner with three or four other girls, all about the same age and behaving similarly, although LaDonna certainly stood out. First was due to her height, which was almost a foot taller that the other girls. Also notable was her physique, for this was not the asexual, formless body of a pre-pubertal 8-year-old, but the fully developed curves and shapes of a young woman. She approached me with a child's hop in her stride, incongruently accompanied by bouncing, fully developed breasts. It appeared that she needed help with a toy that was the center of her attention at that moment. I quickly solved the problem and was immediately rewarded with a genuine hug, pure in its childhood innocence. Normally, such a hug around the waist from an 8-year-old is cause for a smile and a paternal pat on the head. In this case however, feeling the pressure from her breasts, and having difficulty reconciling the age and behavior of the child from the appearance of the woman, I found myself uncomfortable, to the point of pushing her away.

If precocious puberty is recognized and brought to the attention of a properly qualified care provider, the treatment is simple and very effective. A drug that is normally used to turn off the ovaries is administered to the child, resulting in immediate arrest of the development. The medication is continued, as a monthly injection, until the chronologic age catches up with the physical age, at which point the medication is stopped, the maturation resumes, and the normal development continues into adulthood.

Critically, the child's psychological development advances in step with everything else. If however, the intervention is delayed significantly, or in the case of LaDonna, withheld until the process is nearly complete, the result is the incongruent body of a woman with the mind of a child trying to digest the sexual attention that suddenly rears its head all around her. And while the child is tall compared to other children her age, her growth spurt will cease prematurely, and her final height, when she reaches adulthood, will be significantly less than would have been destined by her genetics. In the meantime, the path to adulthood will be fraught with the risk of sexual abuse. LaDonna had her precocious puberty arrested before the onset of her menses, the last step in the transition of puberty. Had her treatment been delayed a few more months, her menses would have started, which by definition means that her body would have started producing eggs.   And since everything else is intact, in place, and functioning as an adult, LaDonna could easily have become pregnant. This exact sequence of events led to the record for the youngest mother: a 6-year-old who was raped, and gave birth in Peru in the 1930's. There have been other, equally tragic cases since then.

I never saw LaDonna again, but thought often of the pretty and innocent child, cursed prematurely with the body of a woman, playing naively in the mean and selfish streets of Newark, New Jersey, and giving unintended sensual hugs to total strangers. I prayed that she at least had a guardian angel watching over her.

* * *

Sandy had no such issues, as she had developed along the same lines as her peers. First the breast buds changing into an adult woman's breasts, then the skin pigment changes, the hair changes, the body odor changes, and finally the alteration in the deposition and distribution of fat. But long after her peers began their menstrual cycles, Sandy remained free of the toils of the monthly bleeding. She was already athletic, and it is well known that strenuous, sustained exercise (as well as malnutrition and extreme weight loss) will shut off the menstrual cycle, and this was perfectly acceptable to a young, healthy, athletic female who couldn't be bothered. And when she joined the military out of high school, the lack of periods was a blessing, and no one bothered to ask 'why'?

That is until Sandy met Doug, found love, and they married while still enlisted. As the end of their tours loomed, and they began to consider a family, and suddenly the lack of menses over all these years began to trigger concern. This in turn led to their visit to my office.

Any proper medical evaluation begins with the history. And in this case, the history, except for the aforementioned issue, was unremarkable. Sandy had no other concerns. Her weight had been stable for a number of years, and was well within the normal range for her height. She suffered no visual changes or persistent headaches, both of which can be a sign of abnormalities within the deep brain structures that control menstrual cycles. Her sex drive and experiences were perfectly normal, and neither partner has noted any issues. Interestingly, Sandy had never bothered to get a Pap smear, having only had the one sexual partner. And as a consequence, no one had ever performed a pelvic exam.

The second part of any medical evaluation is the physical examination. There's a famous saying that if you give a carpenter a hammer, suddenly every problem resembles a nail. It turns out if you're a gynecologist, everything is diagnosed within the pelvis, with help from a speculum and a manual examination. While the statement is facetious, when it comes to reproduction, there is a lot of truth to this, and in the case of Sandy, one problem became immediately obvious: She did not have a cervix. Her vagina, which was somewhat shorter than would be expected in a sexually active female her age, was in reality a blind sac. This had never created a problem since the tissues that make up the vagina are very compliant, ultimately being able to allow a full-term fetus to pass through. But there was no cervix. And the manual examination was suspicious for an absent uterus as well. She also had a fullness in the lower part of her abdomen, on both sides, just in front of the crease of her thigh. A little more pronounced on the right, and both sides somewhat tender on pressure. And come to mention it, during her years in the service she had noted the tenderness on occasional when she was hit in the area, but she assumed that was normal for everyone.

* * *

In the fetus, early during development when the final sex has been determined and the differentiation started, a number of changes take place that culminate, at birth, to the statement "it's a girl!". When the female fetus is only 10-weeks old, and the legs are in place, a dimple begins to push in between the legs, at the site of the future vagina. This dimple, over the next two to three weeks, elongates into a tube (in boys of course, this dimple never appears). At the same time, inside the body, a set of primitive structures also begin changing[1]. These structures can be thought of as formless tubes, one on each side of the body. The highest outer point of the tubes reaches out to the sides and approaches a clump of cells, the future gonads. As the fetus grows, the latter differentiate into the future ovaries, and the former become recognized as the fallopian

---

[1] Very early, before differentiation, the fundamental parts are present for either sex. If female, the male building blocks will atrophy, and if male, the opposite will happen. Often bits of the primitive structures of the other sex remain. When this happens, they present in the adult as odd cysts alongside the internal reproductive structures.

177

tubes. Meanwhile the inner, central half of the tubes meet in the midline, fuse and form the future uterus and cervix, and a small portion of the upper vagina. As the upper tube portion of the vagina reaches down, it meets the dimple, now well developed as a tube reaching up, and the separation between them breaks down, forming the vagina. And suddenly, thru the miracle of differentiation, what was once just a clump of cells has now developed all the necessary parts to participate in future childbearing and perpetuation of the species.

That is, when everything works the way that it should.

And the vast majority of time, it does just that. Occasionally the tube on one side or the other doesn't develop, and one ends up with only one fallopian tube and a uterus that's half the normal size[1]. These women frequently go on to have perfectly normal adulthoods and normal fertility, child bearing and birth. Often the abnormality is only discovered when some other condition invites a closer look. What can be more interesting is when both sides develop normally, but the fusion in the mid-line doesn't take place.

Depending on the extent and the degree of failure, it can cover the entire spectrum from a uterus that has a heart shape, to a double uterus, to a double uterus with a double cervix, to complete duplication of everything, including the full length of the vagina, all the way to the opening. The external genitals do not involve fusion, and are therefore not duplicated.

Now there's some fodder for trash journalism and late-night comedians.

---

[1] Interestingly, the development of the kidney and urinary system closely follow the respective half of the developing tube and uterus. In the vast majority of cases, failure of development of one reproductive half is accompanied by failure of development of the urinary system on the same side.

Lisa, who was besides herself

Lisa was a patient I had the pleasure of seeing in consultation for an unrelated matter, who turned out to be the most interesting example of reproductive organ duplication.

She presented as a delightful young lady, who had recently given vaginal birth, and her chart revealed an abnormal Pap smear in the beginning of her pregnancy. After getting her rather unremarkable history, I proceeded with the speculum examination, also unremarkable, and a repeat Pap smear. Her cervix, having recently dilated to allow the passage of a baby, had the characteristic appearance of tearing and post-birth healing. During her manual examination, something felt unusual along the vaginal wall, and there was a small mass next to her cervix. I repeated the speculum examination, more carefully, and again everything seemed normal. As I slowly removed the instrument, this time I saw a flap of tissue slide by. Now having a clear direction for continuing the examination, I was able to tease the flap back into view, at which point it turned out the flap was actually a midline separation. And on the other side? Another vagina, ending in a cervix. A cervix that had never had to deal with the passage of a 7-some pound baby, and was virginal in appearance. And I held no doubt that above this cervix was also a uterus, much smaller than its twin, again for never having had to carry a fetus. And no doubt extending beyond this a normal fallopian tube, and a normal ovary. Lisa had been sexually active for over seven years, had Pap smears on a yearly basis for most of that time, and the abnormality was not noted until pregnancy and birth caused enough changes for it to become obvious at examination. (I'd love to know if her Pap smears before her pregnancy were always of the same cervix, or alternated at random, but alas there's no way to find out, and the Pathologist would surely scorn me for asking).

Some would consider these women to have double of everything, but in reality, there is no duplication, only failure of fusion. But since everything has an incredible ability to stretch and grow, these women can enjoy normal intercourse, become pregnant in due time, and give vaginal birth. They are at higher risk of giving birth early (since the uterus cannot stretch with the same ease, and to the same degree as a normal, fused organ), and their babies are at risk of being small for age at birth (for the same reason). One of the many problems that can arise in the interim include difficulty with intercourse, since their partner has one of two directions to take at penetration. Upon questioning, Lisa admitted that occasionally she would feel a sharp pain at the beginning of intercourse, representing her husband's indecisiveness in direction (but, as is often the case, this was ignored as normal, perhaps secondary to her husband's physique. I cannot say I hated rupturing his smug balloon).

Once diagnosed, Pap smears have to be a double affair, which doesn't sound so complicated, until you have to deal with an insurance company, arguing why one woman needs two Pap smears every exam.

And, of interest only to Lisa and future medical residents in Obstetrics, the dilemma at her next attempt at pregnancy, for if at that time Lisa's partner should tend toward the right, her pregnancy and birth will proceed along the easier and less complicated lines of a second pregnancy; if he veers to the left, it will be as if she was a first-time mom, with all the attendant risks and complications. Of course, the proper solution is to cut out the wall separating the two vaginas, and leave it all to chance. But first the situation had to be explained to Lisa, then to Lisa's primary physician, and finally to Lisa's incredulous husband, who needs to come in for another appointment, if only to hear the explanation for himself.

It should also be pointed out that while complete failure of fusion is a rare finding, mild forms of incomplete fusion are quite common, suspected to be present in as many as one out of every four women. These frequently present as a heart shaped uterus, because the failure is in the upper most point of fusion. Interestingly, the only complication associated with the mild forms is persistent breech baby at term - thought to be due to interference with the normal rotation of the full-term baby into the head down position. It's difficult to diagnose at the time of cesarean, since the normal stretch of the uterus at term hides the external appearance of the condition. One would have to feel the inner upper part of the uterus carefully after delivery to find out.

* * *

Finally, there's another rare condition, this time involving the receptor of the signal for the male hormone, Testosterone. This defect is genetic, and it is always a mutation, since the presence of the condition precludes reproduction and passage to future generations.

These children are conceived as males, since the Y-chromosome signal and receptor are normal, and while still in the fetal stage develop all of the normal internal male organs. But due to the Testosterone receptor defect, the normal testes are not able to exert their influence on the baby's external features, so the fetus develops into the default sex, and is born a girl.

The other influence of Testosterone is to signal the testes to descend thru the abdomen, via an opening in the muscles of the abdominal wall, and into the future scrotum. Again, because of the receptor defect, this descent is incomplete, and the testes end up in the abdomen or somewhere along the path that they should have taken.

The child, identified at birth as a girl, continues to develop along those lines. And then puberty arrives, and the Testosterone levels begin to increase. Once again, the failure of the feedback mechanism (due to the same receptor defect) causes the levels to rise many times above normal. And then something interesting happens. The blockage of the signal at the receptor is complete, so the male tissues never respond, but due to the structural similarity in the two hormones, Testosterone and Estrogen, as the Testosterone levels continue to markedly increase, the Estrogen receptors, which are normal, do begin to respond to the massive levels of the male hormone that is present.

As a result, the girl continues her development into an adult female, completely normal externally in every way. However, the internal female organs, having been suppressed in the beginning by the Y-chromosome factor, cannot develop at this point, and the internal male parts, besides the testes, are really rather insignificant in size, since they also did not experience any appropriate stimulation during development.

And this brings us back to Sandy.

While she was a perfectly normal appearing female externally, she lacked any internal organs that would allow pregnancy. She did not even have ovaries, so there was no hope of surrogacy, when a female, unable to reproduce, has her eggs fertilized and then implanted in the uterus of a volunteer.

* * *

Sandy's suspected condition was subsequently confirmed with a genetic test, showing her to have a normal male chromosome complement. And the final irony was the necessity for rather urgent surgery, for the lumps that were noted in her groin were her incompletely descended testes. Irrespective of causing her discomfort, they needed to be expeditiously removed. Testes must live their lives at a temperature lower than the rest of the body, hence their location in the scrotal sac, outside the body proper. If this need is not met, there exists a significant risk of a nasty form of cancer developing within the retained organs. In boys with un-descended testes they are surgically relocated into the scrotum as soon as diagnosed, to prevent this cancer from developing. If they need to be removed, the procedure is performed after puberty, to allow that process to successfully complete.

* * *

Sandy had her follow-up visit two weeks later, when all the information on her case had been gathered. Once again, she was attended by her husband, both sitting at comfortable attention, waiting for the results and the recommendation on how to pursue pregnancy when the time was right.

I had spent some time rehearsing what to say to this expectant, attractive and happy young couple. First blow, the fact that she would never be able to bear his child, no matter how aggressive or expensive the intervention; second, that she would need surgery in the very near future to protect her from risk of death from a nasty form of testicular cancer; and the final knockdown, brought out by their insistence on knowing the underlying condition, the fact that Sandy, while still Sandy, was in fact an X-Y individual, although that did not imply diminished female characteristics or identification.

I took great care to explain to Doug that the woman he had married was still there, unchanged except for her inability to conceive. At this point Sandy was in tears, Doug appeared in shock, and after some more questions and explanations, they awkwardly arose, mumbling about getting a second opinion, and shuffled out.

The transformation in their demeanor was complete.

I never saw them again, but hoped that they worked thru this bump in life, and that an unfortunate quirk of nature did not change who they were, or how they felt about each other.

Miscellaneous Topics

The ovary usually occupies a quiet spot in the abdomen, and goes about doing its chores without drawing much attention to itself. Of course, the consequences of its actions are quite noticeable, but the ovary itself rarely causes issues for the woman. She may feel a sharp abdominal pang on one side or the other at the time of ovulation, but even that is usually, in most women, minor and transient. The only time the ovary draws undue attention is when it is enlarged. While the diagnosis of 'enlarged ovary' usually triggers anxiety and brings up thoughts of cancer, in the vast, vast majority of cases, the cause is benign and self-limiting.

We throw out the term ovarian cyst freely, but what is the definition? Medically, an ovarian cyst is a well-defined enlargement within the ovary, that is completely fluid filled. Since this definition includes the normal follicle during its course of development, we use roughly one inch as the normal limit. Anything over that gets stamped as a cyst. Anything over roughly two inches is an abnormal cyst[1]. They can be remnants of a follicle that failed to ovulate, or a left-over cavity, from an ovulation, that filled with blood, which takes a while to reabsorb. Unless particularly large, abnormal in appearance on ultrasound, or causing significant symptoms, they are best left alone and allowed to clear on their own. On the other hand, a cyst in a post-menopausal woman needs investigation, for there is no normal reason for her to have one.

Any mass within the ovary that is solid, or has solid components, is not normal and needs prompt investigation, whether the patient is young or old. Solid or mixed masses are concerning because they can represent a cancer, or a tumor with the potential to degrade into a cancer.

And then there are the interesting alternatives.

---

[1] And then there are the spectacularly large cysts. See page 197.

Of Hair and Teeth, and Mandi & Brandi

Mandi was a quiet 19-year-old young lady living at home while attending classes at our local community college. She was also a member of her school's volleyball squad, which turned out to be the source of her issues. She was brought into the office by her mother after repeated complaints of the sudden onset of a severe lower right abdominal pain, lasting a few minutes, usually while active on the volleyball court. The last episode had nearly resulted in an ambulance call, but the pain had just as suddenly resolved, and she was embarrassed by all of the attention. Her mother's maternal instincts had led to an appointment and the visit.

I found Mandi to be rather shy, and during my visit with her, without the presence of her mother, she had vehemently denied ever being sexually active. Her bright red innocent blush and her gaze and body language convinced me that she was being truthful, and the usual pregnancy test ruled out that possibility. The other routine tests, and the cultures for sexually transmitted infections, would have to wait a bit.

A review of any medical text will reveal entire chapters on the various causes of lower quadrant abdominal pain, especially on the right side, for that is the location of the appendix in most of the population[1]. As a demonstration of the complexity of the diagnosis, the causes can range from skin pain (think 'Shingles'), to muscle pain, to myriad bowel issues, to kidneys and associated collecting system. Also in the mix are nerve

---

[1] I say 'most', because there are a few people out there whose internal organs are reversed. In the simplest case, the bowels are reversed, with the appendix on the left side; in the most severe cases, the entire abdomen and chest are reversed, with the heart beating away on the right side. Listening to the chest of one of these individuals, you would momentarily suspect that they were dead, as there would be no heartbeat, even while they're sitting on the examining table blinking away at you.

impingements and spinal issues. And, just to keep things interesting, mental issues, ranging from discreet diseases of the nervous system, to physical manifestations of psychological issues, to attention getting behavior for whatever reason or gain the patient obtains.

Associate the pain with a female, and now you also have the reproductive organs to consider, especially the tubes and ovaries.

The only way to find one's way thru the forest and to the path of the right diagnosis is to begin with a thorough history. In this case the patient's age, the sudden onset and equally sudden resolution of the symptoms, and their relatively short duration, along with absence of associated or residual effects, left most bowels and urinary causes as unlikely. The association with vigorous activity would tend to lead one in the direction of muscle pain and ache issues, but the sudden spontaneous resolution made that diagnosis also unlikely, unless the source was cramps. However, most people can readily identify a muscle cramp, and this was not the case.

My biggest concern at this point was an ovarian torsion.

* * *

The ovaries are metaphorically suspended in the air[1]. Their main support is a ligament that runs from the upper outer pole of the ovary to the side of the pelvis, and carries the main blood supply. They are also attached to the uterus at their inner, lower pole by a thin filament, also containing a collateral blood supply. Contrary to popular misconception, the Fallopian tube is not attached to its respective ovary, rather dangling next to it[2].

---

[1] Picture a towel drying on a clothes line.
[2] See plate-19.

This arrangement allows some freedom of motion for the ovary, and allows eggs to be released from almost anywhere along its surface. It can, especially in the presence of vigorous activity, also result in the ovary flipping over and twisting upon its support, a condition that can lead to mild pain. Once twisted, further activity will usually lean towards reversing the twist, and the symptoms resolve.

But occasionally the ovary will twist multiple times in the same direction, worsening the pain, and slowly strangulating the blood supply, which then leads to excruciating pain. The condition is known as an 'ovarian torsion', and can become a medical emergency, both for the severity of the symptoms and the possibility that the ovary will die from lack of blood supply, ultimately affecting fertility[1].

Fortunately, ovarian torsion in women is rather uncommon. What can increase the risk is any condition that asymmetrically enlarges the ovary, such as a larger than usual follicle, a large cyst, or a tumorous mass. While ovarian cancer in a young woman is a very rare occurrence, the most common non-malignant tumorous mass in a young woman is a Cystic Teratoma, also known as a Dermoid cyst.

Going back to the developing embryo at around eight weeks of gestation, we have seen how a small collection of cells in the future pelvis are given instructions to form the gonad, eventually staying put and becoming the ovaries, or descending into the scrotum and becoming testicles[2]. The primitive cells within the ovaries that will become future eggs are

---

[1] Being anatomically similar, but in a different location, the male testicle can also twist around its pedicle, leading to 'testicular torsion' and similar symptoms. Interestingly, even though it's in a completely different location in the body, the similar origin of the testicle and ovary in the embryo result in the associated pain being felt in the same area of the abdomen in males and females.
[2] See page-53, 'The cycle'.

undifferentiated at this point, and if put in the right environment, can develop into any tissue of an adult or, if prodded appropriately, even a complete person.

Normally these cells are given instructions to follow the appropriate path and develop into follicles, and future eggs. But sometimes, for reasons that are not understood, some of these cells ignore their destiny. They develop along the lines of another person, but given their location and abnormal development, the signals are confused, or incomplete, or erroneous, or most likely, a combination of all three. The cells therefore develop into adult tissues, but not a separate being[1]. And, again for reasons that are not understood, these adult tissues are usually tissues associated with, or derived from, skin.

While benign teratomas usually develop in an ovary, or the testes in the male, they can develop from any left-over primordial cells located anywhere, and have been reported in all areas of the body, including extremities, liver, lungs, the brain, and even the eye, and their symptoms are mostly due to the physical effect of their mass. Within the ovary, there are few restrictions to growth, and they can achieve impressive sizes, until their physical size, or its consequence, such as torsion, makes their presence known.

Even more bizarre, sometimes the teratomas develop adult type glands.

Most commonly these are skin associated glands, such as the glands that produce the thick lubrication of skin and hair shafts[2], but they

---

[1] In its extreme and very rare form, the teratoma develops into a 'Fetus-in-fetu', and progresses into left-right differentiation, sometimes with a spinal column and neuronal tissue. Brain tissue has not been reported. It has a completely different origin from an absorbed or parasitic twin.
[2] Sebaceous glands, producing sebum.

occasionally can be functional glands, such as the thyroid. Picture a small growth, symptom free, deep within the ovary, that has its own thyroid gland that doesn't pay attention to the normal regulatory signals of the body, and merrily pours out thyroid hormone. All the while the patient and her physician grow weary trying to figure out why her thyroid level is high, when her normal thyroid gland is obedient and quiet.

And while the teratoma is composed of well-defined adult type tissues, given the origin of the abnormality, and the abnormal location, the risk of transformation into a cancer is significant, and not to be ignored.

* * *

One of the most difficult gynecologic exams are the ones that are necessary on a young, post-pubertal, sexually naïve female. The patients are mortified, and unable to relinquish any control to the examiner. The first battle is getting them into the gown, and then getting their feet into the examining table stirrups. After an unremarkable abdominal exam (itself a significant battle of wills), and knowing Mandi's history, and discerning her level of modesty, I did not even attempt a pelvic examination, settling instead for an office ultrasound[1]. The examination of the offending site was significant for the presence of a large mass with multiple internal divisions, and the presence of solid components. Surgical evaluation was unfortunately the only option.

I had read and reviewed teratomas many times during my training, but had never actually seen one. During Mandi's surgery, her right ovary was about the size of a tomato (normal is about the size of a walnut), enlarged

---

[1] I've learned to give the young patients a sense of control over the situation by respecting their modesty and allowing them to insert the probe into the vagina without any assistance from me. At that point I take over the manipulation, but at no time do I need to visually or manually examine them.

with a mass surrounded by a wall. Fortunately, the mass was easily removed intact, and the defect in the ovary repaired with minimal damage to the normal tissues, and hopefully no effect on her future fertility. The rest of the surgery was unremarkable, and Mandi was transferred to recovery. Thus, safely out of the body and in a tray, the mass was opened[1].

Inside, it was filled with a dense collection of long, dark hair, intermixed with a thick, white creamy material which turned out to be sebum, the product of sebaceous glands, which lubricate and protect skin and hair shafts. Imagine 19 years without a haircut or a bath. The pathologist reported the presence of numerous deformed teeth and bundles of nerve tissue. The good news was that all of the components were normal adult type tissues, and no further treatments were indicated.

I reviewed what I felt were the fascinating surgical findings with Mandi and her family afterwards. Her mother was almost as impressed as I was, asked all sorts of questions, and in the end, she named the teratoma 'Brandi'. Mandi seemed to be bored and distracted, but I found out later that the typical reaction, in a young woman, of such a report is more of a revulsion or disgust at the thought of something growing inside that has hair and teeth.

I wished Mandi well, and hoped that she went on to have a healthy relationship and as many babies as she desired, free from further interference from Brandi.

---

[1] One has to take great care in removing any ovarian mass, for in the case of an undiagnosed cancer, its inadvertent rupture can seed the pelvis with malignant cells, and significantly increase the risk of poor long-term outcome.

Immortality

At conception, the life duration of the future individual is definitively laid down. The clock, so to speak, is wound at conception and immediately begins to wind down. It appears that the longest life a human can hope to achieve is around 110 to 120 years, tops. In the beginning of recorded history, average life expectancy was around 30-35 years, but some individuals lived into their late 60's or early 70's. By the 18th Century, average life expectancy has risen to around 45, but some individuals lived into their late 60's or early 70's. Today, average life expectancy in the United States for women is around 80, but some individuals reach 100 to 110.

This timetable is programmed somewhere within the cells, and so far, the search for the key (the fountain of youth, as it were) has been elusive. You can certainly shorten the lifespan with poor lifestyle choices, but how to prolong it remains a mystery. Research has shown that at some level, all cells in the body are programmed to reproduce a set number of times, after which the cells will stop reproducing and eventually die[1]. Even cancer cells, with their propensity to divide beyond the original programmed number, have a limit on their ability to continue their existence.

With one exception.

In early 1951 a woman, Henrietta Lacks[2], presented to Johns Hopkins University for treatment of advanced cervical cancer. Her cancer, resisting treatment, eventually spread and she died shortly thereafter. Some of the cancer cells that were taken during her biopsies actually

---

[1] Indeed, every living complex organism on Earth, plant or animal, has a life limit.
[2] Her real name.

193

appear quite normal, but when cultured, and to this day, those cells continue to divide and propagate[1].

For the first time in medical history, an immortal human cell line was identified. The source of the immortality remains elusive, but during the transformation into cancer, the built-in life limit time bomb in some of her cells was somehow defused. Whether this transformation can be applied to a fetus remains to be seen, but we now know that, at least on a cellular level, immortality is a possibility[2].

Whether this treatment should ever be practiced remains an argument for the ethicists. Youth is not just a phase of life; it is also the time when the brain, still plastic and not set in its ways, is best capable of creative thought and original solutions for ongoing problems[3]. One should shudder at the thought of how the advancement of civilization would slow to a crawl, or stop, if the population consisted of stodgy ancient folks, set in their ways and resistant to change, even if physically healthy[4].

Perhaps there is a very good underlying reason why cells, and by extension, organisms, are programmed with a set life expectancy.

---

[1] The culturing and subsequent research into her cells was done without her consent or any compensation to her or her estate. This remains a dark stain on an otherwise bright area of research. I refer the reader to *The Immortal Life of Henrietta Lacks*, by Rebecca Skloot; Crown (2011).

[2] The application of immortality treatment would have to occur in utero, perhaps at the time of conception. Immortality in cells after birth is one of the hallmarks of cancer.

[3] Yes, I know there are exceptions. But they are the exception, not the rule.

[4] In all aspects- technology, science, medicine, law, etc.

Feedbacks and Systems

Women, without being flippant, have some unique characteristics. This is not an expression of the obvious, but a statement about physiology. One of my medical school instructors once pointed out that there are only two human examples of a positive feedback system, and both of these are found in women.

First, some explanations.

Every system in the body that has a supervising regulatory function is controlled by negative feedback. Every single one. Eat a large meal and when digestion is complete and the meal hits the blood stream the blood sugar goes up, so the body secretes insulin from the pancreas. The minute the insulin secreting cells crank up, another system begins to crank them down[1], for otherwise the insulin would outrun the blood sugar and the person would collapse from low blood sugar, and eventually die. When you get excited, your body secretes hormones to crank up heart rate and blood pressure. The instant these hormones hit the blood stream another system begins to counteract them, for without the negative feedback the increasing blood pressure and heart rate would lead to an inevitable heart attack. Every system has a negative feedback in place, for without control (or worse, a positive feedback), something would have to create an endpoint, or the organism would rapidly expire.

Except for the two systems found in women.

The first example is the ovary, close to the time of ovulation. As the now dominant follicle grows, its sensitivity to the signaling hormone also

---

[1] Glucagon, also from the pancreas.

increases[1], which in turn increases the Estrogen secreted. This increased Estrogen level feeds back and dials down the signaling hormone, but at the same time, it stimulates (positive feedback) a second signaling hormone[2]. This signal axis does not have a down regulator. The only end point to this example of a positive feedback system is the rupture of the follicle and release of the egg, the act of ovulation, which puts a brake to everything.

* * *

The second example is found during labor. The contractions of the uterus are stimulated by a signaling hormone from the brain[3]. This hormone is in turn driven by the mother's subconscious perception of the contractions. This is one reason why pregnant women, in a coma at term, frequently will not go into active, spontaneous labor.

As a result, the system that drives the contractions is stimulated in turn by the contractions themselves, with no dial down system in place. This is one reason why contractions during labor tend to progressively increase in intensity and frequency. The only limit on the process is fatigue of the uterine muscle, and the only end point is the delivery of the baby, which causes a marked reduction in the size of the uterus, release of the tension on the uterine wall, and signals a stop to the cycle[4].

---

[1] FSH: follicle stimulating hormone, from the pituitary of the brain.
[2] LH: luteinizing hormone, also from the pituitary of the brain.
[3] Oxytocin, also from the pituitary of the brain. What triggers the initiation of the labor process remains a mystery.
[4] There are other, unfortunate endpoints, such as uterine exhaustion or rupture. Neither has a happy outcome.

Miscellaneous Tidbits

Some interesting records, collected from journal publications and relevant medical sites. I tried to avoid internet gossip and drivel columns. And yes, some of these records may very well be invalid by the time of this reading.

First documented abdominal hysterectomy

1843, in England. Patient did not survive.

1853, in the United States. First documented case with patient survival.

First vaginal hysterectomy

About 120AD. Outcome unknown. Many vaginal hysterectomies were carried out throughout the centuries, usually for uterine inversion. Patients rarely survived.

Largest ovarian tumor

132-lb benign mucinous cyst, completely fluid filled, removed in 2018 in Connecticut. Patient lost over 170 pounds afterwards from the mass and associated abdominal fluid.

Largest uterine fibroid

29-lb, removed in 2011 from a 68-year-old (documented).

61-lb, removed in 2018 from a 57-year-old (undocumented).

Biggest baby – born alive

22-pounds at birth[1] (Guinness world record), born in 1879 in Ohio. Mother was a Giantess, at nearly 8-feet tall.

---

[1] There is a record of a 24-pound delivery in Minnesota in the 1800's. Baby was stillborn.

Biggest baby – vaginal delivery

See previous entry!

Smallest baby – liveborn & survived

244gms (8.6 ounces; about the weight of a small apple) born at 23-weeks of gestation, December 2018 in San Diego. Normal weight for a baby at 23-weeks of gestational age is about 600gms (21 ounces, or 1.3 pounds)[1].

Most prolific mother

44 (confirmed), born to a mother in Uganda, thru 2016. Includes three sets of quadruplets, four sets of triplets, and six sets of twins. Yams had nothing to do with it[2].

69 (dubious), born to mother in Siberia, thru 1765.

Most babies delivered in one pregnancy – liveborn & survived

Eight, January 2009 in California. Who can forget "Octomom", Nadya Suleman.

Nine, in 2021, to Halima Cisse in Morocco. All are alive, as of this writing.

Longest duration between births of twins

90 days, January 1, & March 30, 1996[3].

---

[1] Part of the miracle of this baby's survival is no doubt due to the stress it was enduring in the uterus, hence the poor weight gain, and the urgency for the extremely premature delivery. See Plate-12B for a similar example.
[2] See page 124.
[3] See page 141.

Longest duration between births of triplets

Five days, December 28, 2019 & January 2, 2020. The interval between the first delivery and the subsequent two means the triplets were born in different years, as well as different decades.

Youngest mother

Six years old at delivery, in Peru, 1939. The girl suffered from precocious puberty[1].

Oldest mother at time of birth – via IVF procedure

Aged 74, in India. The reasons for the procedure defy explanation[2].

Oldest mother – natural conception

Aged 59, in United Kingdom
Aged 68, in China[3] (dubious record regarding mother's age)

First in-vitro baby

July, 1978 in Manchester, England. The baby, Louise Brown, went on to have two children of her own as an adult, both naturally conceived.

First designer baby

Born in Colorado, in 2000. Baby was an IVF pregnancy, conceived to provide donor marrow to his older sister who was suffering from a blood cancer. The transfer was successful, and both babies did well. The ethical storm, however, continues. Designer babies, selected as a form of essential

---

[1] See page 175.
[2] I have a hard time understanding the desire on the part of the mother or the willingness on the part of the physician. Unless, of course, the goal was publicity or internet fame.
[3] It would be difficult to think of a medical condition that would allow a woman to ovulate at this advanced an age.

embryo screening for genetic diseases and conditions that cannot be treated, continues unabated[1]. Non-essential designer babies, as in cases of selection for eye color, height, etc., are currently banned in most countries that have the technology to carry out the screening.

Life expectancy, female

Average is about 80 years of age, for women in the United States, as of 2019. There is significant difference in life expectancy based on race and financial standing. Worldwide, as of this publication, the best life expectancy for women is found in Monaco (at 90 years of age) followed by Japan and Singapore. Far from being at or near the top, the United States is somewhere around number 40.

---

[1] Most of the controversy surrounding these procedures have to do with the fact that unneeded or diseased embryos are subsequently destroyed.

Most preposterous

In 2001 I met a Russian Perinatologist who claimed that in the 1980's the GDR (German Democratic Republic, more commonly known as East Germany) was working on having males carry & deliver babies[1]. I spent some time looking for confirmation, and failing to find any, decided the story was an urban legend. However, the question to be asked is: could it be done?

And the answer, given today's technology, is 'yes'.

First the male would have to have hormone therapy for preparation, then the embryo, created via IVF, would be injected into the abdomen. Continued hormone administration would allow the fetus that successfully implants onto the omentum to continue growth and development[2].

Once successfully implanted, the fetus and placenta would create all the necessary signals to maintain the pregnancy. Delivery would of course be via Cesarean. The discomfort, social stigma, serious risks, and long-lasting hormonal side-effects would probably rule out volunteers for the procedure.

---

[1] For what reason was never explained.
[2] See page 94.

Dr. George Nicholas Papanicolaou (1883-1962)
Over a ten-year period, he meticulously observed and recorded changes
in the cells of the cervix leading to cancer. Using that knowledge, he
then developed a simple, cheap and easily applied screening test, the Pap
smear. As a result, cervical cancer tumbled from the number one cause of
cancer death in women. One of the true giants of medicine, and to
whom countless cervical cancer survivors owe a debt of gratitude.

A representative bill, for an uncomplicated vaginal delivery, in 1953. Includes six days of hospitalization for mother and newborn.

In case one is tempted to blame inflation, it should be noted that $102 in 1953, adjusted for inflation, would equal about $1,080 today. The same delivery today, limited to two days, would cost, depending on the locale in the United States, anywhere from $13,000 to $35,000, or more.

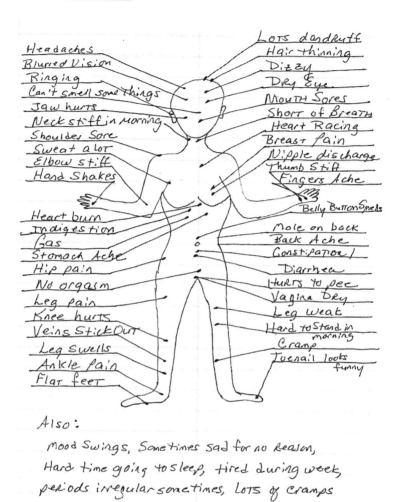

List of complaints and concerns, presented by a patient on her first visit. She was hoping to have everything addressed, by a Gynecologist, within the confines of her 1-hour appointment. This was not an elderly individual, ravaged by the passage of time, but a healthy and fit, mid-30's woman, in what should have been the prime of life.

She left less than satisfied and somewhat disappointed.

Statistics

Top Three Causes of death, in order of frequency, for women, in the United States, by age[1]

Aged 1 to 20[2]

1. Unintentional injuries[3]
2. Cancer
3. Suicide

Aged 20-45

1. Unintentional injuries
2. Cancer
3. Heart disease

Aged 45-65

1. Cancer
2. Heart disease
3. Unintentional injuries

Aged 65-85

1. Cancer
2. Heart disease
3. Respiratory issues

Aged 85+

1. Heart disease
2. Alzheimer's
3. Cancer

---

[1] Most of the data is from the CDC, for the last year available, which at the time of this writing is 2019. The numbers have not changed significantly in the past decade.

[2] I start the numbers at age 1, because in the first year of life most causes of death, male & female, have to do with prematurity, birth defects, and other birth related causes.

[3] Includes accidents and homicides.

Interesting observations:

- Cancer is in the top three categories for all ages.
- Unintentional injuries are in the top three categories from ages one thru 65.
- Suicide is number three from adolescence until age 20[1]. Not because women kill themselves regularly and successfully, but because overall they are so healthy that the few that take their own lives bump the numbers up.
- These statistics are for all women. The risks are different if one includes ethnicity. For example, for non-Hispanic Black females, ages one thru 20, the causes of death, in order, are:
  1. Unintentional injuries;
  2. Homicides;
  3. Cancer.

I refer the reader to the CDC website at

https://www.cdc.gov/women/lcod/index.htm

---

[1] From age 15 to 24, for white, non-Hispanic females, suicide is the number 1 cause of death.

United States, leading cause of cancer diagnosis in women, all ages
1. Breast
2. Lung
3. Colon
4. Uterus
5. Thyroid

United States, leading cause of cancer death in women, all ages
1. Lung[1]
2. Breast
3. Colon
4. Pancreas
5. Ovary

Interesting observations:

- Numbers for causes of cancer death are skewed, based on age. For example, from ages one thru 25, the number one cause of cancer death is malignancy of the blood system (Lymphoma, Leukemia), followed by cancers of the nervous system (brain tumors).

- Lung cancer kills more women in the United States than the next two, breast and colon cancer, combined. Stop smoking, and lung cancer drops down to number seven.

- Breast cancer was the number one cause of cancer death in women from 1950's until early 1990. The death rate began a steady decline at that time, and has continued since.

---

[1] Worldwide, breast cancer is the number one cause of cancer death, followed by lung cancer at number two.

Interesting observations (continued):

- Lung cancer was the number seven cause of death for females in the United States until the 1960's, at which point it began a sharp rise which continued thru the beginning of the new millennium. There's little doubt that the rise was due to smoking becoming fashionable for women after World War 2, keeping in mind that it typically takes about 20 years for cancer to develop following exposure to carcinogens such as tobacco smoke. As smoking has decreased in glamour, we are beginning to see a corresponding decline in lung cancer rates in the past 15 years.

- Cervical cancer was the number one cause of cancer death for females in the United States throughout the beginning of the 20th Century. Deaths due to cervical cancer dropped precipitously in the 1950-1960 decade, no doubt due to the widespread use of Pap smear screening[1]. It has leveled off in the past 15 years, but is expected to decline further with the widespread use of the anti-Condyloma (HPV-Human Papilloma Virus) vaccine.

---

[1] A screening test identified and developed by Dr. George Papanicolaou, a little-known name to whom countless women, since the mid-1940's, owe their survival. See page-202.

Glossary

These are definitions for some of the common terms used in this text. I've included this section to hopefully make the reading a bit easier for non-professionals.

Ab- A euphemistic contraction of the word 'abortion', used medically to avoid social stigmas and emotional triggers.

Abortion- A lay term for intentional interruption of a live pregnancy. Medically the term was used in the past to denote any pregnancy interruption or loss, with 'elective abortion' used to describe the procedure as commonly understood in lay terms. Because of the social stigma surrounding the word 'abortion' in any context, it is now almost exclusively used to imply elective.

Baby- A loose term applied to the newborn, commonly used from before birth to the point where the infant begins to walk and is promoted to a 'toddler'. See Neonate, Fetus.

Conception- The successful act of fertilization of the egg with the sperm.

Conceptus- The physical result of a conception.

Contraception- Any means of preventing conception. It can apply to males (condoms, withdrawal) or females (pretty much everything else). It can be short-acting, such as condoms, sponges, spermicides, diaphragms or hormone pills, or long-acting, such as implants or intrauterine devices. Finally, it can be permanent, such as vasectomy in the male or tubal ligation in the female.

D&C- Acronym for 'Dilatation and Curettage'. The dilatation refers to widening of the cervical opening, and the curettage refers to scraping the inside of the uterus with a sharp, curved instrument. This common procedure is used to remove tissue within the uterus. This can include excessive lining, retained placental fragments, retained tissues after a miscarriage, or in the case of an abortion, a healthy pregnancy.

D&E- Similar to a D&C, but instead of a sharp instrument, a large tube with an angled tip is connected to a suction machine and used to obtain similar results.

DNA- The basis for the unit of heredity that defines the organism, from appearance, to function, to behavior. The organism can be a single cell or a human. DNA is the building block of genes, which are carried in separate units called 'chromosomes', which vary in number between species, and sometimes, due to errors, within species. See 'gene', 'genome'.

Doctor- A person who has completed the training, testing, and any additional requirements to earn a doctorate degree. Term is not limited to physicians, who typically have Medical or Osteopathy degrees, but also those who have earned the degree in sciences, philosophy, arts, education, law, religion, or other highly trained fields. See Physician.

Embryo- A developing first trimester pregnancy. See 'fetus'.

Fetal Demise- A miscarriage, after the first trimester, in which the pregnancy is retained, often necessitating surgical intervention for removal.

Fetus- Term used to describe the baby during development in the uterus. Medically, at the moment of fertilization the term 'zygote' is used, until differentiation begins and one can recognize the different layers. Then, during the first third of the pregnancy, the term 'embryo' is used, with 'fetus' being reserved for the remainder of the pregnancy.

Follicle- Term for the developing egg, prior to release from the ovary.

Gamete- Term for the reproductive cell, prior to fertilization. In the female this would be the oocyte, and in the male the sperm.

Gene- A specific segment of a chromosome, specifically dedicated to the production of proteins, signals, structure, or cellular instructions. See 'DNA'.

Genome- The collective blueprint that defines species, and individuals within the species. The genome consists of the entire collection of the organism's unique genes, in turn made up of DNA.

Gestation- Medical term for the pregnancy, comparable to incubation.

Gonad- Medical term for the internal structure producing reproductive cells and associated hormones. In the female, the gonads are the ovaries, and responsible for producing eggs, or ova, and female hormones. In the male, they are the testicles, and produces sperm and testosterone.

Hormone- A signal produced by specialized cells in one area of the body, usually transported via blood, and used to provide a signal to regulate or alter activity for another system or function. Often back regulated by another, reciprocal signal.

Hysterectomy- Surgical removal of the uterus. The cervix can be left behind (incomplete) or taken (complete). Patients often equate 'complete' with removal of the tubes and/or ovaries at the same time, but technically, that defines a different, separate procedure.

Incomplete Ab- A term describing a miscarriage with retention of some of the products of conception. These can include the placenta and amniotic sac or 'membranes'. If the fetus is retained, the term 'Missed Ab' is used. Usually used before the age of viability, with 'retained products of conception' used to describe the condition after viability and delivery. The 'Ab' is derived from 'abortion', but the application of the latter term has been narrowed to elective procedures. See 'abortion'.

Infertility- Failure to achieve pregnancy after appropriate attempts. The medical definition requires one year or longer of unprotected intercourse. There is a tendency to automatically blame the woman, but statistically, when the cause is identified, it lies equally between the two partners.

IVF- Acronym for In Vitro Fertilization, or colloquially, a 'test tube baby'. A procedure for achieving pregnancy in an infertile woman by removing eggs (usually multiple, sometimes dozens), directly from the ovaries. The eggs may be from the patient, or an egg donor. Likewise, the fertilization may be achieved using the partner's sperm or a sperm donor, who commonly remains anonymous. The eggs are fertilized outside of the body, and after confirmation of successful cell division, one or more are injected into the uterus, which has been primed with hormones. The initial eggs are harvested by first overstimulating the ovaries with hormone injections, and once the follicles reach the appropriate size, they are collected using a vaginal procedure. Of course, once the eggs are fertilized, a number of options become available: they can be frozen for later use, they can be donated to other infertile women, or they can be inserted into a surrogate uterus – a rental, so to speak.

Miscarriage- Loss of a pregnancy before the age of viability, about 23-24 weeks of gestation. See 'fetal demise', 'abortion'.

Missed Ab- Medical term used to describe a retained miscarriage in the first trimester. The 'Ab' stands for 'abortion', but because of the implication and social stigma, that term is reserved for elective procedures. As a result, the expression 'missed abortion' has become an archaic term, and no longer used by physicians. See 'incomplete Ab'.

Neonate- Term used to describe a newborn. It's generally applied from birth until some arbitrary time afterwards, usually four to six weeks, or in the case of a premature birth, until four to six weeks after discharge from the nursery.

Nurse- A general term applied to any of the supportive staff in the hospital wards, or the physician's office. The proper use of the term should be limited to those individuals who have the necessary training and certification for a Nursing degree (RN: Registered Nurse, or LPN: Licensed Practical Nurse). There are also specialists in Nursing, such as Nurse Practitioner, and even a PhD in Nursing, although they rightfully would be called 'Doctor' at that point.

Oocyte- The cell produced by the ovary, prior to fertilization.

Ova- Plural of ovum.

Ovum- Term for the egg, from the moment of release from the ovary until fertilization.

Pelvic Exam- A medical examination of the female reproductive system. Usually includes a lower abdominal exam, an external genital examination, a vaginal and cervical examination using a speculum[1], and a bimanual examination, using both hands, one with one or two fingers inserted into the vagina, the other hand on the abdomen. The purpose is to determine any unusual enlargement, displacement, or tenderness of the uterus and attached organs. During pregnancy, the internal examination is used to determine if the fetus has descended into the pelvis, and the integrity of the cervix. Until cervical changes occur in labor, a vaginal ultrasound is much more sensitive and accurate for the latter.

Physician- Term for someone who has the academic education to earn an MD (Medical Doctor) or DO (Doctor of Osteopathy) degree, and usually the clinical training to practice medicine. The term does not distinguish between those who deal with living patients, those who deal with newly deceased patients, those who deal with the tissues of patients, and those who deal with radiologic images of patients. It also includes those who do not deal with patients at all, thru retirement, alternative career paths, or other reasons. Those physicians that deal regularly with patients as well as doctors in training are reverently labeled 'Attending Physicians', usually capitalized for emphasis. Contrast with 'Doctor'

Physician, Attending- A term for the physician taking care of a particular patient or a medical issue of the moment. In a teaching facility, the term, usually capitalized, is applied to the teaching physicians, who take responsibility for the care of the patients, and are knowledgeable enough to teach others. In the eyes of the doctors in training, they are the facility God.

---

[1] Surely derived originally from a torture device. See Plate-1.

Pluripotential Cell- Also known as a Primordial cell, this medical term refers to a primitive cell, usually found in the early developing fetus, that has the capability to mature into any tissue or organ of the body. The only pluripotential cell remaining in the adult is the germ cell, or abnormally, the cells found in certain types of cancers.

Post-Term Pregnancy- Any pregnancy that has completed 42 weeks of gestation, counting from the first day of the last menstrual period.

Pre-Term Pregnancy- Any pregnancy that delivers before 37 weeks of gestation, counting from the onset of the last menstrual period.

Primordial Cell- See Pluripotential cell.

STI- Sexually Transmitted Infection. Any infection that is commonly acquired during sexual activity. Broadly, can include infestations, such as pubic lice or Trichomonas.

Term Pregnancy- Any pregnancy that has completed 37-42 weeks of gestation, counting from the onset of the last menstrual period. See Preterm, Post-term.

Test Tube Baby- See 'IVF'.

Trimester- A convenient reference dividing the pregnancy into three parts. First trimester covers conception to 12 weeks (time of rapid growth and organ development), second trimester 13 weeks to 28 weeks (time of organ and tissue maturation), and third trimester 29 weeks until delivery. Each trimester has sentinel events and particular problems and developmental characteristics, making the arbitrary divisions useful.

Ultrasound- In medicine, used to describe a diagnostic procedure, utilizing a machine that allows visualization of internal structures by generating ultra-high frequency sound waves via a probe, and interpreting the resultant echoes. In the setting of Obstetrics & Gynecology, the probe can be applied abdominally (on the skin), or inserted into the vagina, which yields much higher resolution images of the pelvic organs, as well as the pregnancy up until the second trimester. The procedure also avoids many of the risks of x-rays when a pregnancy is present[1]. Modern 3-D and 4-D ultrasound examinations allow visualization of surfaces, often used to obtain impressive images of the fetus within the uterus, and live action sonograms. The appeal of the latter has led to the establishment of commercial ultrasound sites, frequently in shopping centers, whose sole purpose (outside of profits) is to create mementos for the expectant mother[2]. A common term used to describe these procedures is 'keepsake ultrasound'.

Zygote- The cell released from the ovary, after fertilization has taken place, before implantation. see 'embryo', 'fetus'.

---

[1] There have been concerns raised about repeated or prolonged effect of ultrasound examinations, especially during the early pregnancy. The intense, high frequency sound waves are known to generate local temperature increases, and induce or alter fluid motion within the gestation, and generate cavitation. The only current recommendation is to use ultrasound examination judiciously and limit the duration of exams.
[2] One of the concerns raised about commercial ultrasound examinations is how they handle any potential or perceived abnormalities noted during the exam.

Photo credits

- Plate-1: Author
- Plate-2: Author, data from ACOG.
- Plate-3: Author, data from ACOG.
- Plate-4, A & B: Author
- Plate-5: Author
- Plate-6, A & B: Author's collection
- Plate-7, A: Author
- Plate-7, B: Patient, used with permission.
- Plate-8, A & B: Author
- Plate-9, A & B: Author
- Plate-10, A: Pausefrance.fr - Used with permission
- Plate-10, B: Prezi.com - Used with permission
- Plate-11: Author
- Plate-12, A: Elpatagonico.com - Used with permission
- Plate-12, B: Connor Florio - Used with permission
- Plate-13: Author
- Plate-14, A: Mastology, 2018;28(2):106-9
- Plate-14, B: Wikipedia
- Plate-15, A: Surgeryzone.net - Used with permission
- Plate-15, B: Plasticsurgerykey.com - Used with permission
- Plate-16, A: Ensherahnews.ir - Used with permission
- Plate-16, B: Eskuvokiallitasok.hu - Used with permission
- Plate-17: Author
- Plate-18, A: Author
- Plate-18, B: Author
- Plate-19: Author, data from ACOG.
- Plate-20: Author's grandchildren.

Rear cover: Author's first grandson, at 6-months of age.